CURRICULUM LINKED

Teaching writing skills

Read — Analyse — Plan

Narratives

Recounts

Reports

Procedures

Explanations

Discussions

6265C

PRIMARY WRITING *(Book F)*

Published by Prim-Ed Publishing 2008
Reprinted under licence by
Prim-Ed Publishing 2008, 2014
Copyright© R.I.C. Publications® 2006
ISBN 978-1-84654-110-0
PR–6265

Additional titles available in this series:
PRIMARY WRITING *(Book A)*
PRIMARY WRITING *(Book B)*
PRIMARY WRITING *(Book C)*
PRIMARY WRITING *(Book D)*
PRIMARY WRITING *(Book E)*
PRIMARY WRITING *(Book G)*

Internet websites
In some cases, websites or specific URLs may be recommended. While these are checked and rechecked at the time of publication, the publisher has no control over any subsequent changes which may be made to webpages. It is *strongly* recommended that the class teacher checks *all* URLs before allowing pupils to access them.

View all pages online

Website: www.prim-ed.com

Primary writing

BOOK F

Foreword

Primary writing is a series of seven books designed to provide opportunities for pupils to read, examine and write a variety of text types; narratives, recounts, procedures, reports, explanations and discussions.

Titles in this series:

- *Primary writing* Book A
- *Primary writing* Book B
- *Primary writing* Book C
- *Primary writing* Book D
- *Primary writing* Book E
- *Primary writing* Book F
- *Primary writing* Book G

This book is also provided in digital format on the accompanying CD.

Contents

Teachers notes

Six text types have been chosen:
- narratives
- recounts
- procedures
- reports
- explanations
- discussions

Three examples of each text type are given for pupils to read and analyse.

Following each example, a framework is provided for pupils to use in planning and writing that text type.

Each text type is presented over four pages:
- ~ teachers page
- ~ pupil page – 1 includes an example of the text type
- ~ pupil page – 2 uses a framework for analysing the text type on pupil page – 1
- ~ pupil page – 3 provides a framework for the pupil to write his or her own example of the particular text type

Teachers page

The text type and number of the example are given.

The parts of each text type are given with relevant information for the teacher.

Teacher information provides suggestions for using the worksheet in the classroom and ideas for display, publishing, purposes for writing, appropriate audiences and the context in which pupils may be asked to write the particular text type.

Some examples of language features used in each text type are indicated. Also see pages vi – vii.

Answers are provided for pupil page – 2 where the pupils are analysing the text type.

Teachers notes

Pupil pages

Pupil page – 1

The text type and number of the example are given.

The text type example is supplied.

Artwork appropriate to the example is provided.

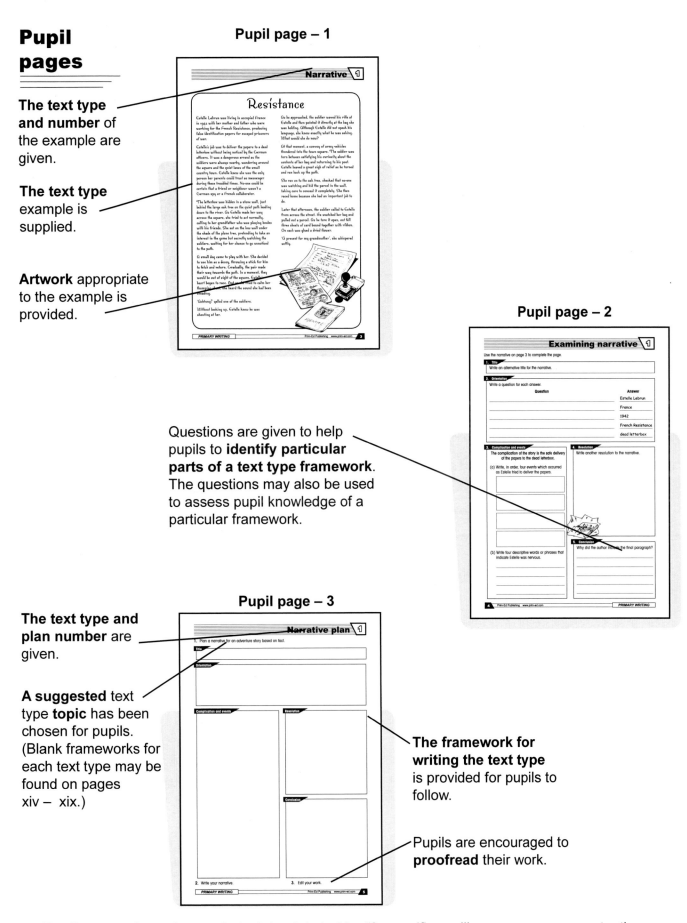

Questions are given to help pupils to **identify particular parts of a text type framework**. The questions may also be used to assess pupil knowledge of a particular framework.

Pupil page – 2

Pupil page – 3

The text type and plan number are given.

A suggested text type **topic** has been chosen for pupils. (Blank frameworks for each text type may be found on pages xiv – xix.)

The framework for writing the text type is provided for pupils to follow.

Pupils are encouraged to **proofread** their work.

- **Pupil page – 1** may be used at a later date to identify specific spelling, grammar or punctuation examples, as a reading comprehension activity or reading assessment.

Writing format information

Below are general descriptions of the text types included in this book.

Report

– is a framework which describes aspects of a living or non-living thing in detail
– includes:
  - **Title**
  - **Classification**: a general or classifying statement
  - **Description**: accurate and detailed
  - **Conclusion**: a comment about the content of the report (optional)
– uses the following **language features**:
  - factual language rather than imaginative
  - the third person
  - the timeless present tense
  - information organised into paragraphs

A report may be written in the form of a book review, scientific report, newspaper or magazine article, eyewitness account or a progress report.

Recount

– is a framework which retells events as they happened in time order
– may be factual, personal or imaginative
– includes:
  - **Title**
  - **Orientation**: all relevant background (who, when, where, why)
  - **Events**: significant events in detail
  - **Conclusion**: often with an evaluative comment
– uses the following **language features**:
  - vocabulary to suggest time passing
  - paragraphs to show separate sections
  - the past tense

A recount may be written in the form of a newspaper report, diary, letter, journal, eyewitness account, biography, autobiography or history.

Narrative

– is a framework which tells a story
– includes:
  - **Title**
  - **Orientation**: the setting, time and characters
  - **Complication**: involving the main character(s) and a sequence of events
  - **Resolution**: to the complication
  - **Conclusion**: often showing what has changed and what the characters have learnt
– uses the following **language features**:
  - a range of conjunctions to connect ideas
  - appropriate paragraphing
  - descriptive language
  - usually written in past tense

A narrative may be written in the form of a poem, story, play, imaginative story, fairytale, novel, myth, legend, ballad, science fiction story or modern fantasy.

Procedure

– is a framework which outlines how something is made or done
– includes:
  - **Title**
  - **Goal**: the purpose of the procedure shown clearly and precisely
  - **Materials**: a list of materials or requirements under appropriate headings or layout
  - **Steps**: the method in a detailed, logical sequence
  - **Test**: an evaluation (if appropriate)
– uses the following **language features**:
  - instructions often with an imperative verb
  - subject-specific vocabulary
  - simple present tense
  - concise language

A procedure may be written in the form of a recipe, instructions for making something, an experiment, an instruction manual, a maths procedure, how to play a game, how to operate an appliance, how to use an atlas or how to deal with a problem.

Writing format information

Explanation

– is a framework which outlines how something occurs, works or is made

– includes:
  - **Title**
  - **Statement**: precisely what is to be explained
  - **Explanation**: a clear account in logical sequence of how and why the phenomenon occurs
  - **Conclusion**: an evaluation and comment about what has been explained

OR

  - **Title**
  - a **definition**
  - a **description** of the components or parts
  - the operation—how it works or is made
  - the application—where and when it works or is applied
  - special features—interesting comments
  - evaluation or comment/**conclusion**

– uses the following **language features**:
  - subject-specific terms and technical vocabulary where appropriate
  - simple present tense is often used
  - linking words to show cause and effect
  - information is organised into paragraphs

An explanation may be written in the form of an essay, or a handbook—for example, how a kite works—a science, health or geography text.

Discussion

– is a framework which argues for a particular position and attempts to persuade the audience to share this view

– includes:
  - **Title**
  - **Overview**: statement of the problem or issue and the writer's position
  - **Arguments**: presented in a logical manner with supporting detail, usually from the strongest to the weakest
  - **Conclusion**: a restating of the writer's position and a summary of the arguments presented

– uses the following **language features**:
  - a variety of controlling and emotive words and conjunctions
  - paragraphs to state and elaborate on each point

A discussion may be written in the form of an essay, a letter, policy statement, a critical review, an advertisement, an editorial or a speech.

Modelled writing

The role of the teacher is to observe and support pupils as they develop as writers.

Writing is an extremely complex activity, simultaneously involving decisions on content, text coherence and cohesion, spelling, grammar, punctuation and a sense of audience and purpose. Because it takes time and practice to develop understanding of the writing process and the different writing formats, many opportunities for pupils to interact with their teacher and their peers are essential.

Modelled writing is an effective way of supporting pupil writers, particularly when the focus is on the cognitive processes involved.

Frequent modelling of the planning process and how these plans can be used to write text in different formats, is strongly recommended.

Writing format checklists

Pupil **narrative** checklist

☐ ☐ ☐ ☐   ☐ ☐   ☐   ☐   ☐ ☐ ☐ ☐ ☐ ☐

Title:

☐ The title is appropriate and interesting.

Orientation:

☐ The characters are introduced and described.

☐ Information about where the story happened is provided.

☐ The time the story took place is stated.

Complication and events:

☐ The complication involving the main characters is explained.

☐ The sequence of events is described.

Resolution:

☐ A logical, believable resolution is presented.

Conclusion:

☐ The narrative has a satisfactory ending.

Writing skills:

☐ The narrative is written in the past tense.

☐ Descriptive language is included.

☐ Vocabulary is varied and interesting.

☐ A range of conjunctions connects ideas.

☐ Paragraphs are used to introduce new ideas.

☐ Punctuation and spelling have been checked.

Name: _____ Date: _____

Pupil **narrative** checklist

☐ ☐ ☐ ☐   ☐ ☐   ☐   ☐   ☐ ☐ ☐ ☐ ☐ ☐

Title:

☐ The title is appropriate and interesting.

Orientation:

☐ The characters are introduced and described.

☐ Information about where the story happened is provided.

☐ The time the story took place is stated.

Complication and events:

☐ The complication involving the main characters is explained.

☐ The sequence of events is described.

Resolution:

☐ A logical, believable resolution is presented.

Conclusion:

☐ The narrative has a satisfactory ending.

Writing skills:

☐ The narrative is written in the past tense.

☐ Descriptive language is included.

☐ Vocabulary is varied and interesting.

☐ A range of conjunctions connects ideas.

☐ Paragraphs are used to introduce new ideas.

☐ Punctuation and spelling have been checked.

Name: _____ Date: _____

Writing format checklists

Pupil **recount** checklist

☐

Title:

☐ The title is suitable.

Orientation:

☐ ☐ A clearly written orientation provides relevant information about who, when, where and why.

Events:

☐ Significant events are described in detail.

☐ Events are retold in chronological order.

Conclusion:

☐ The ending is clearly described.

☐ An evaluative comment about the conclusion is included.

Writing skills:

☐ Paragraphs are used to show separate sections.

☐ Descriptive language is included.

☐ Vocabulary suggests the passing of time.

☐ The past tense is maintained.

☐ Sentence beginnings vary.

☐ Quotation marks are used for quoted speech.

☐ Punctuation and spelling have been checked.

Name: _____ Date: _____

Pupil **recount** checklist

☐

Title:

☐ The title is suitable.

Orientation:

☐ ☐ A clearly written orientation provides relevant information about who, when, where and why.

Events:

☐ Significant events are described in detail.

☐ Events are retold in chronological order.

Conclusion:

☐ The ending is clearly described.

☐ An evaluative comment about the conclusion is included.

Writing skills:

☐ Paragraphs are used to show separate sections.

☐ Descriptive language is included.

☐ Vocabulary suggests the passing of time.

☐ The past tense is maintained.

☐ Sentence beginnings vary.

☐ Quotation marks are used for quoted speech.

☐ Punctuation and spelling have been checked.

Name: _____ Date: _____

Writing format checklists

Pupil **report** checklist

Title: _____

Classification: ☐
A general or classifying statement about the subject of the report is included.

Description: ☐ ☐ ☐
Accurate, detailed descriptions are provided.
Information is clearly presented.
Facts are relevant and interesting.

Conclusion: ☐
A personal comment is made about the subject.

Writing skills: ☐ ☐ ☐ ☐ ☐ ☐
Language is factual rather than imaginative.
The report is written in the third person.
The present tense is used.
Technical vocabulary and subject-specific terms are used.
Information is organised in paragraphs.
Punctuation and spelling have been checked.

Name: _____ Date: _____

Pupil **report** checklist

Title: _____

Classification: ☐
A general or classifying statement about the subject of the report is included.

Description: ☐ ☐ ☐
Accurate, detailed descriptions are provided.
Information is clearly presented.
Facts are relevant and interesting.

Conclusion: ☐
A personal comment is made about the subject.

Writing skills: ☐ ☐ ☐ ☐ ☐ ☐
Language is factual rather than imaginative.
The report is written in the third person.
The present tense is used.
Technical vocabulary and subject-specific terms are used.
Information is organised in paragraphs.
Punctuation and spelling have been checked.

Name: _____ Date: _____

Writing format checklists

Pupil **procedure** checklist

Title:

Goal:
☐ The purpose is clearly and precisely stated.

Materials:
☐ The materials or requirements are listed under appropriate headings or layout.

Method:
☐ The steps are clear and concise.
☐ There is a logical order to the sequence of the steps.
☐ The steps are easy to understand and follow.
☐ All the necessary steps are included.

Test:
☐ An evaluation to test if the procedure has been successfully followed is included.

Writing skills:
☐ Some instructions begin with command verbs.
☐ The present tense is used.
☐ Unnecessary words are omitted.
☐ Punctuation and spelling have been checked.

Name: _____ Date: _____

Pupil **procedure** checklist

Title:

Goal:
☐ The purpose is clearly and precisely stated.

Materials:
☐ The materials or requirements are listed under appropriate headings or layout.

Method:
☐ The steps are clear and concise.
☐ There is a logical order to the sequence of the steps.
☐ The steps are easy to understand and follow.
☐ All the necessary steps are included.

Test:
☐ An evaluation to test if the procedure has been successfully followed is included.

Writing skills:
☐ Some instructions begin with command verbs.
☐ The present tense is used.
☐ Unnecessary words are omitted.
☐ Punctuation and spelling have been checked.

Name: _____ Date: _____

Writing format checklists

Pupil **explanation** checklist

☐ ☐ ☐☐☐ ☐ ☐☐ ☐☐

Title:

Definition:

A precise statement or definition is provided.

Description:

A clear account of how and why the phenomenon occurs is included.

Information is relevant and correct.

Information is provided in a logical order.

Explanations are clearly and simply stated.

Concluding statement:

The conclusion includes an evaluation or comment.

Writing skills:

Linking words are used to show cause and effect.

The simple present tense is used.

Technical vocabulary and subject-specific terms are used.

Information is organised in paragraphs.

Spelling and punctuation have been checked.

Name: _____ Date: _____

Pupil **explanation** checklist

☐ ☐ ☐☐☐ ☐ ☐☐ ☐☐

Title:

Definition:

A precise statement or definition is provided.

Description:

A clear account of how and why the phenomenon occurs is included.

Information is relevant and correct.

Information is provided in a logical order.

Explanations are clearly and simply stated.

Concluding statement:

The conclusion includes an evaluation or comment.

Writing skills:

Linking words are used to show cause and effect.

The simple present tense is used.

Technical vocabulary and subject-specific terms are used.

Information is organised in paragraphs.

Spelling and punctuation have been checked.

Name: _____ Date: _____

Writing format checklists

Pupil **discussion** checklist

Title: _____

□ □□□ □□ □□□□

Overview:

The opening statement presents the issue and the writer's position.

Arguments:

Arguments are presented in a logical manner.

Supporting information is provided.

The strongest arguments are presented first.

The language is persuasive.

Conclusion:

A summary of the supporting arguments is given.

An evaluative comment is presented.

Writing skills:

Paragraphs state and elaborate each point.

Controlling and emotive language is used.

A variety of conjunctions is used.

Punctuation and spelling have been checked.

Name: _____   Date: _____

Pupil **discussion** checklist

Title: _____

□ □□□ □□ □□□□

Overview:

The opening statement presents the issue and the writer's position.

Arguments:

Arguments are presented in a logical manner.

Supporting information is provided.

The strongest arguments are presented first.

The language is persuasive.

Conclusion:

A summary of the supporting arguments is given.

An evaluative comment is presented.

Writing skills:

Paragraphs state and elaborate each point.

Controlling and emotive language is used.

A variety of conjunctions is used.

Punctuation and spelling have been checked.

Name: _____   Date: _____

Blank writing format – Narrative

Title

Orientation

Who? When? Where? Why?

Complication and events

Resolution

How was it solved?

Conclusion

Blank writing format – Recount

Title

Orientation

Who? Where? When? Why?

Events

Conclusion

Blank writing format – Procedure

Title

Goal

Materials

Steps

Test

How will you know if your procedure works?

Blank writing format – Report

Title

Classification

What is it?

Description

Conclusion

What I think about it.

Blank writing format – Explanation

Definition

What it is.

Description

Conclusion

What I think.

Blank writing format – Discussion

Title

Overview

What is the topic?

What is my point of view?

Arguments

Conclusion

Prim-Ed Publishing   www.prim-ed.com

Proofreading and editing checklist

Name: _____   Date: _____

Title: _____   Text type: _____

Punctuation:

I have included:

    capital letters for:

        beginning sentences. .... ☐

        proper nouns. .... ☐

        titles. .... ☐

    question marks. .... ☐

    full stops. .... ☐

    commas:

        in lists . ... ☐

        for pauses . ... ☐

        to make meaning clear .... ☐

    apostrophes:

        for grammatical contractions. .... ☐

        to show ownership. .... ☐

    exclamation marks. .... ☐

    quotation marks. .... ☐

    colons:

        in titles . ... ☐

        for offset lists . ... ☐

    brackets .... ☐

    hyphens .... ☐

Spelling:

I have:

        checked the spelling of any unknown words. .... ☐

        not confused words that sound the same. .... ☐

        used correct endings for plurals. .... ☐

Language features:

I have included:

        a variety of different verbs. .... ☐

        correct verb tenses. .... ☐

        correct verb-subject agreement. .... ☐

        appropriate adverbs to describe verbs. .... ☐

        suitable nouns .... ☐

        appropriate pronouns .... ☐

        interesting adjectives .... ☐

        suitable conjunctions .... ☐

        a variety of prepositions .... ☐

        appropriate paragraphing .... ☐

        no double negatives .... ☐

Writing:

I have read through my writing to check that:

        it makes sense. .... ☐

        it is easy to understand. .... ☐

        there are no repeated or omitted words. .... ☐

        there are no errors of fact. .... ☐

Class recording sheet

Date: ✓ developed • developing ✗ not yet	Pupils																														
NARRATIVES																															
Title is appropriate																															
Characters are described																															
Setting is outlined with some details																															
Complication is explained																															
Resolution is realistic and believable																															
Conclusion with character outcomes																															
RECOUNTS																															
Orientation is provided																															
Events are clearly described																															
Events are sequenced logically																															
Conclusion is relevant to context																															
PROCEDURES																															
Goal is stated																															
Materials are listed																															
Steps are inclusive and sequential																															
Language is clear and concise																															
REPORTS																															
Subject is classified																															
Information is relevant and organised																															
Facts are accurate																															
A final comment is included																															
EXPLANATIONS																															
Subject is defined																															
Information is coherent and relevant																															
Vocabulary is precise																															
Information is organised logically																															
DISCUSSIONS																															
Topic and writer's position stated																															
Arguments are logical and justified																															
Language is persuasive																															
Arguments and position summarised																															
WRITING SKILLS																															
Spelling is usually correct																															
Chooses precise, appropriate vocabulary																															
Uses correct punctuation																															
Verb tense is correct and sustained																															
Ideas are relevant and organised																															
Shows sense of purpose and audience																															
Edits and proofreads writing																															

Curriculum links

England
English – Writing (Texts)

Book	Year	Objectives
A	1	• write sentences by saying out loud what they are going to write about • sequence sentences to form short narratives • re-read what they have written to check that it makes sense • discuss what they have written with the teacher or other pupils • read aloud their writing clearly enough to be heard by their peers and the teacher • leave spaces between words • join words and sentences using and • begin to punctuate sentences using a capital letter and a full stop, question mark or exclamation mark • use a capital letter for the names of people, places, the days of the week and the personal pronoun 'I'
B	2	• write narratives about personal experiences and those of others (real and fictional) • write about real events • write for different purposes • plan what they are going to write about • write down ideas and/or key words, including new vocabulary • encapsulate what they want to say, sentence by sentence • evaluate their writing with the teacher and other pupils • re-read to check that their wiring makes sense and that verbs to indicate time are used correctly and consistently, including verbs in the continuous form • proof-read to check for errors in spelling, grammar and punctuation • read aloud what they have written with appropriate intonation to make the meaning clear • learn how to use both familiar and new punctuation correctly including full stops, capital letters, exclamation marks, question marks, commas for lists and apostrophes for contracted forms
C & D	3 & 4	• plan their writing by discussing writing similar to that which they are planning to write in order to understand and learn from its structure, vocabulary and grammar • discuss and record ideas • compose and rehearse sentences orally (including dialogue) • build a varied and rich vocabulary and an increasing range of sentence structures • organise paragraphs around a theme • in narratives, create settings, characters and plot • in non-narrative material, use simple organisational devices such as headings and sub-headings • evaluate and edit by assessing the effectiveness of their own and others' writing and suggesting improvements • evaluate and edit by proposing changes to grammar and vocabulary to improve consistency • proof-read for spelling and punctuation errors • read aloud their own writing, to a group or the whole class, using appropriate intonation and controlling the time and volume so that the meaning is clear
E–G	5–6	• identify the audience for and purpose of the writing, selecting the appropriate form and using often similar writing as models for their own • plan their writing by noting and developing initial ideas, drawing on reading and research where necessary • in writing narratives, considering how authors have developed characters and settings in what they have read, listened to or seen performed • select appropriate grammar and vocabulary, understanding how such choices can change and enhance meaning • in narratives, describe settings, characters and atmosphere and integrating dialogue to convey character and enhance action • use a wide range of devices to build cohesion within and across paragraphs • use further organisation and presentational devices to structure text and to guide the reader • assess the effectiveness of their own and others' writing • propose changes to vocabulary, grammar and punctuation to enhance effects and clarify meaning • ensure the consistent and correct use of tense throughout a piece of writing • ensure correct subject and verb agreement when using singular and plural, distinguishing between the language of speech and writing and choosing the appropriate register • proof-read for spelling and punctuation errors • perform their own composition, using appropriate intonation, volume, and movement so that meaning is clear

Curriculum links

Northern Ireland
Language and Literacy – Writing

Book	Year	Objectives
A	2	• observe the teacher modelling specific writing strategies • use stories as models for structuring their own writing • write in a range of genres with teacher guidance • begin to show evidence of sequence in recount and instructions
B & C	3 & 4	• participate in modelled and independent writing • talk about and plan what they are going to write • begin to check their work in relation to specific criteria • write for a variety of purposes and audiences • express thoughts and opinions in imaginative and factual writing
D–G	5–7 Extension	• participate in modelled and independent writing • discuss various features of layout in texts and apply these, as appropriate, within their own writing • write for a variety of purposes and audiences, selecting, planning and using appropriate style and form • use the skills of planning, revising and redrafting to improve their writing • express thoughts and opinions in imaginative and factual writing • begin to formulate their own personal style

Wales
English – Writing

Book	Year	Objectives
A & B	1 & 2	• organise and present imaginative and factual writing in different ways, helpful to the purpose, task and reader and incorporating some of the different characteristics of forms that are used • plan and review their writing, assembling and developing their ideas and presenting their writing clearly • write with increasing confidence, fluency and accuracy • write in a range of genres, incorporating some of the different characteristics of these forms
C–G	3–6 Extension	• use the characteristic features of literary and non-literary texts in their own writing, adapting their style to suit the audience and purpose • draft and improve their work and present writing appropriately • write for a range of purposes, for a range of real or imagined audiences, in a range of forms and in response to a range of stimuli

Curriculum links

Republic of Ireland
English Language – Writing

Book	Class	Objectives
A	Senior Infants	• receive help from the teacher, who will sometimes act as a scribe • write frequently, write for different audiences and see writing displayed • see the teacher model writing as an enjoyable experience • write about everyday experience or about something just learned • write stories
B & C	1st/2nd Class	• experience a classroom environment that encourages writing • observe the teacher as he/she models writing stories • experience how a story structure is organised by reading and listening to fiction • write regularly for different audiences, explore different genres and have writing valued • experience an abundance of oral language activity when preparing a writing task • realise that first attempts at writing are not necessarily the finished product and learn to undertake second drafts in order to improve writing • write in a variety of genres, write about something that has been learned, write the significant details about an event or an activity, write an explanation for something and write stories
D & E	3rd/4th Class	• experience a classroom environment that encourages writing • observe the teacher modelling different writing genres • use reading as a stimulus to writing • write stories that explore a variety of genres • receive and give positive responses to writing and see his/her writing valued • experience varied and consistent oral language activity as a preparation for writing • learn to use questions as a mechanism for expanding and developing a story • give sequence to ideas and events in stories • develop an appreciation of how the intended audience should influence the nature of a piece of writing • learn to revise and redraft writing • write in a variety of genres with greater sophistication • write down directions on how to perform a particular process and create stories
F & G	5th/6th Class	• experience a classroom environment that encourages writing • observe the teacher model a wide variety of writing genres • experience interesting and relevant writing challenges • receive and give constructive responses to writing and see his/her writing valued • experience a level of success in writing that will be an incentive to continue writing • experience varied and consistent oral language activity as part of the pre-writing process • observe the teacher improving writing • write independently through a process of drafting, revising, editing and publishing • choose a register of language and presentation appropriate to subject and audience • write in a variety of genres and write for a particular purpose and audience • argue the case in writing for a particular point of view • write stories

Curriculum links

Scotland
Literacy and English – Writing

Book	Level	Objectives
A–C	First	• enjoy exploring and discussing text structures • appreciate the richness of language and texts • write independently, use appropriate punctuation and order sentences in a way that makes sense • check writing makes sense throughout the writing process • present writing in a way that will make it legible and attractive for the reader • use notes and other types of writing to help create new text • consider the type of text being created and select ideas and information, organise these in a logical sequence and use interesting words • convey information, describe events or processes, share opinions and persuade the reader in different ways • explore the elements writers use in different genres and use this to compose stories with interesting structures, characters and/or settings
C–F	Second	• enjoy exploring and discussing text structures • appreciate the richness of language and texts • use appropriate punctuation, vary sentence structures and divide work into paragraphs • check writing makes sense and meets its purpose throughout the writing process • consider the impact that layout and presentation have • use notes and other types of writing to create new text • consider the type of text being created and select ideas and information, organise these in an appropriate way for the purpose and use suitable vocabulary for the audience • use language and style to engage and/or influence the reader • convey information, describe events and explain processes in different ways • persuade, argue, explore issues or express an opinion using relevant supporting detail and/or evidence • write for different purposes and readers • explore the elements writers use in different genres and use this to compose stories with an interesting and appropriate structure, interesting characters and/or settings which come to life
F–G	Third	• enjoy exploring and discussing increasingly complex texts and structures • appreciate the influence texts can have • punctuate and structure different types of sentences and arrange these into paragraphs • review and edit writing to ensure it meets its purpose and communicates meaning throughout the writing process • consider the impact that layout and presentation will have on the reader • use notes and other types of writing to create original text • consider the type of text being created and select ideas and information, organise these in an appropriate way for the purpose and use suitable vocabulary for the audience • engage and/or influence readers through use of language, style and tone as appropriate to the genre • convey information, describe events and explain processes or concepts • persuade, argue, evaluate, explore issues or express an opinion, using a clear line of thought and relevant supporting detail and/or evidence • explore the elements writers use and compose texts in different genres, using some of the conventions of chosen genre successfully and/or creating convincing narratives, characters and settings

Structural and language features are shown on the left and right of the text below.

Title	Resistance	
Orientation – who, when, where, why	Estelle Lebrun was living in occupied France in 1942 with her mother and father who were working for the French Resistance, producing false identification papers for escaped prisoners of war. Estelle's job was to deliver the papers to a dead letterbox without being noticed by the German officers. It was a **dangerous** errand as the soldiers were always nearby, wandering around the square and the quiet lanes of the small country town. Estelle knew she was the only person her parents could trust as messenger during these **troubled** times. No-one could be certain that a friend or neighbour wasn't a German spy or a French collaborator.	• varied and interesting adjectives; e.g. **dangerous**, **troubled** • appropriate paragraphing
Complication and significant events – in detail	The letterbox was hidden in a stone wall, just behind the large oak tree on the quiet path leading down to the river. **As** Estelle made her way across the square, she tried to act normally, calling to her grandfather who was playing boules with his friends. She sat on the low wall under the shade of the plane tree, pretending to take an interest in the game but secretly watching the soldiers, waiting for her chance to go unnoticed to the path. A small dog came to play with her. She decided to use him as a decoy, throwing a stick for him to fetch and return. Gradually, the pair made their way towards the path. In a moment, they would be out of sight of the square. Estelle's heart began to race. But as she tried to calm her thumping chest, she heard the sound she had been dreading. 'Achtung!' yelled one of the soldiers. Without looking up, Estelle knew he was shouting at her. As he approached, the soldier waved his rifle at Estelle and then pointed it directly at the bag she was holding. Although Estelle did not speak his language, she knew exactly what he was asking. What would she do now?	• a range of conjunctions to connect text; e.g. **As**, **but** • descriptive language; e.g. **thundered**, **convoy**
Resolution – to the complication	At that moment, a **convoy** of army vehicles **thundered** into the town square. The soldier was torn between satisfying his curiosity about the contents of her bag and returning to his post. Estelle heaved a great sigh of relief as he turned and ran back up the path. She ran on to the oak tree, checked that no-one was watching and hid the parcel in the wall, taking care to conceal it completely. She then raced home because she had an important job to do.	• verbs in the past tense; e.g. **snatched**, **was glued**
Conclusion – indicating what has changed	Later that afternoon, the soldier called to Estelle from across the street. He **snatched** her bag and pulled out a parcel. As he tore it open, out fell three sheets of card bound together with ribbon. On each **was glued** a dried flower. 'A present for my grandmother', she whispered softly.	

Teacher information

- Discuss what a narrative is, explaining that it may be presented in many forms; e.g. play, poem, fable.
- Read and discuss the narrative on page 3 with the pupils. Explain what a dead letterbox is and how it has been used in the past by spies and secret societies.
- Discuss the different sections of the framework and ensure pupils understand how the text fits into each one.
- Emphasise the language features listed to the right of the text above.
- Work through the analysis on page 4 with the pupils.
- Plan a similar narrative, writing ideas for each section within the framework and discuss and model how the plan is transformed into a coherent piece of text.
- Pupils use page 5 to plan and then write an adventure story based on fact, involving an element of personal danger.
- Pupils write a narrative based on a topic they are currently studying in history. (Context)
- Examples of pupils' work may be bound in a book as a resource for other classes studying the topic. (Publishing/Purpose/Audience)
- Narratives may be framed with silhouettes of maps or

objects relevant to the text and displayed with other work from the topic, demonstrating a cross-curricular approach to teaching. (Display)

Answers

Page 4

1. Teacher check
2. Teacher check
3. (a) Estelle pretended to watch her grandfather play boules.
   She watched and waited for her chance to go, unnoticed to the path.
   She played 'throw and catch' with a dog.
   She was stopped by the soldier.
   (b) Teacher check
4. Teacher check
5. Answers may include: To tie up the loose end. To show how clever Estelle was and how much danger she faced.

Resistance

Estelle Lebrun was living in occupied France in 1942 with her mother and father who were working for the French Resistance, producing false identification papers for escaped prisoners of war.

Estelle's job was to deliver the papers to a dead letterbox without being noticed by the German officers. It was a dangerous errand as the soldiers were always nearby, wandering around the square and the quiet lanes of the small country town. Estelle knew she was the only person her parents could trust as messenger during these troubled times. No-one could be certain that a friend or neighbour wasn't a German spy or a French collaborator.

The letterbox was hidden in a stone wall, just behind the large oak tree on the quiet path leading down to the river. As Estelle made her way across the square, she tried to act normally, calling to her grandfather who was playing boules with his friends. She sat on the low wall under the shade of the plane tree, pretending to take an interest in the game but secretly watching the soldiers, waiting for her chance to go unnoticed to the path.

A small dog came to play with her. She decided to use him as a decoy, throwing a stick for him to fetch and return. Gradually, the pair made their way towards the path. In a moment, they would be out of sight of the square. Estelle's heart began to race. But as she tried to calm her thumping chest, she heard the sound she had been dreading.

'Achtung!' yelled one of the soldiers.

Without looking up, Estelle knew he was shouting at her.

As he approached, the soldier waved his rifle at Estelle and then pointed it directly at the bag she was holding. Although Estelle did not speak his language, she knew exactly what he was asking. What would she do now?

At that moment, a convoy of army vehicles thundered into the town square. The soldier was torn between satisfying his curiosity about the contents of her bag and returning to his post. Estelle heaved a great sigh of relief as he turned and ran back up the path.

She ran on to the oak tree, checked that no-one was watching and hid the parcel in the wall, taking care to conceal it completely. She then raced home because she had an important job to do.

Later that afternoon, the soldier called to Estelle from across the street. He snatched her bag and pulled out a parcel. As he tore it open, out fell three sheets of card bound together with ribbon. On each was glued a dried flower.

'A present for my grandmother', she whispered softly.

Use the narrative on page 3 to complete the page.

1. Title

Write an alternative title for the narrative.

2. Orientation

Write a question for each answer.

Question	Answer
_____	Estelle Lebrun
_____	France
_____	1942
_____	French Resistance
_____	dead letterbox

3. Complication and events

The complication of the story is the safe delivery of the papers to the dead letterbox.

(a) Write, in order, four events which occurred as Estelle tried to deliver the papers.

[ ]

[ ]

[ ]

[ ]

(b) Write four descriptive words or phrases that indicate Estelle was nervous.

_____

_____

_____

4. Resolution

Write another resolution to the narrative.

5. Conclusion

Why did the author include the final paragraph?

_____

_____

_____

_____

1. Plan a narrative for an adventure story based on fact.

Title

Orientation

Complication and events

Resolution

Conclusion

2. Write your narrative.

3. Edit your work.

The text below has the features indicated.

Title	**Accidental find**
Orientation – who, when, where, why	*Paul and Rosa are on a quiet, early summer beach holiday with their parents. They are leaning against some rocks, dangling their feet in a pool and gazing out at the **sparkling** ocean.*
Complication and significant events – in detail	Paul: *(standing up and walking away)* I'm so bored, Rosa. Let's find something to do before I go mad! Rosa: *(jumping up)* Wait for me! Let's go exploring! *The two walk along the beach **until** they see some caves.* Rosa: *(excitedly)* Let's have a look in here and see how far these caves go. *Paul and Rosa enter a cave **which** opens into a large chamber.* Paul: Hey! There's another chamber after this one, and a passage. It's too dark though. I can't ... *Paul lets out a **terrifying** cry and Rosa hears him falling.* Rosa: Paul! Are you okay? Can you hear me? Paul! Paul! Answer me! Paul: *(weakly)* Yeah. I'm fine but I can't see a thing. Go back to the house and bring the torches. Quickly! *Rosa rushes back and soon returns with the torches and their parents.* Dad: *(shining a torch)* Paul! Can you hear me? Paul: Down here, Dad. Be careful! *Dad shines the torch and locates him, lying on the ground, having fallen down a hole about two metres deep. There is blood on his forehead.*
Resolution – to the complication	Dad: *(climbing down to Paul)* Goodness me, son! What happened to you? Hey! What's this here? Bones! Huge bones! I'd say something pretty big died down here, quite some time ago! I wonder what they're from? We'll have to get someone out to investigate. Paul: Who knows, Dad? Maybe some prehistoric mammal. That'd be so cool! *Dad helps Paul to his feet. He groans in pain but is able to **clamber** out of the hole where Mum and Rosa **are waiting** anxiously.* Mum: *(gently)* Here Paul, let me look at you. I'll clean up that cut. It doesn't look too bad. Paul: Dad, tell them about the bones! *Dad makes a call to the police and **explains** their discovery. Within the hour, the area is roped off and Paul is interviewed by a local reporter.*
Conclusion – indicating what has changed	*Later that day:* Dad: *(after answering his mobile)* It's the museum, Paul. It seems your idea of a prehistoric mammal wasn't far off the mark! They want you to interview you on television. Are you interested? Paul: *(excitedly)* You bet, Dad! Wow! Now this holiday is starting to get interesting!

- varied and interesting adjectives; e.g. **sparkling**, **terrifying**

- a range of conjunctions to connect text; e.g. **until**, **which**

- appropriate paragraphing

- descriptive language; e.g. **clamber**

- verbs in the past tense; e.g. **explains**, **are waiting**

Teacher information

- Explain that a play script is a form of narrative which differs from other narratives in its presentation; e.g. stage directions written in present tense.
- Read and discuss the narrative on page 7 with the pupils. Note the method of presenting each character's speech and the use of stage directions.
- Discuss the different sections of the framework and ensure pupils understand how the text fits into each.
- Explain that a framework gives the narrative order and helps the reader to understand the story.
- Emphasise the language features listed to the right of the text above.
- Work through the analysis on page 8 with the pupils.
- Plan a similar narrative, writing ideas for each section within the framework.
- From this plan, discuss and model, with the use of writing skills, how the plan is transformed into a coherent piece of text in the form of a play script.
- Pupils plan then write a play about a holiday adventure using the narrative plan on page 9.

- In small groups, pupils read and perform each play. (Purpose)
- Each group performs its plays to another class. (Audience)
- Each group designs posters advertising its plays, attaching copies of each script. (Display/Publish)

Answers

Page 8

1. Teacher check
2. Who? – Paul, Rosa and their parents
   When? – early summer
   Where? – the beach
   Why? – on holiday
3. (a) Because Paul is bored
   (b) (i) – 4   (ii) – 2   (iii) – 1   (iv) – 3
4. He finds some old bones which turn out to be of historic value.
5. Teacher check

Accidental find

Paul and Rosa are on a quiet, early summer beach holiday with their parents. They are leaning against some rocks, dangling their feet in a pool and gazing out at the sparkling ocean.

Paul: *(standing up and walking away)* I'm so bored, Rosa. Let's find something to do before I go mad!

Rosa: *(jumping up)* Wait for me! Let's go exploring!

The two walk along the beach until they see some caves.

Rosa: *(excitedly)* Let's have a look in here and see how far these caves go.

Paul and Rosa enter a cave which opens into a large chamber.

Paul: Hey! There's another chamber after this one, and a passage. It's too dark though. I can't …

Paul lets out a terrifying cry and Rosa hears him falling.

Rosa: Paul! Are you okay? Can you hear me? Paul! Paul! Answer me!

Paul: *(weakly)* Yeah. I'm fine but I can't see a thing. Go back to the house and bring the torches. Quickly!

Rosa rushes back and soon returns with the torches and their parents.

Dad: *(shining a torch)* Paul! Can you hear me?

Paul: Down here, Dad. Be careful!

Dad shines the torch and locates him, lying on the ground, having fallen down a hole about two metres deep. There is blood on his forehead.

Dad: *(climbing down to Paul)* Goodness me, son! What happened to you? Hey! What's this here? Bones! Huge bones! I'd say something pretty big died down here, quite some time ago! I wonder what they're from? We'll have to get someone out to investigate.

Paul: Who knows, Dad? Maybe some prehistoric mammal. That'd be so cool!

Dad helps Paul to his feet. He groans in pain but is able to clamber out of the hole where Mum and Rosa are waiting anxiously.

Mum: *(gently)* Here Paul, let me look at you. I'll clean up that cut. It doesn't look too bad.

Paul: Dad, tell them about the bones!

Dad explains and makes a call to the police and explains their discovery. Within the hour, the area is roped off and Paul is interviewed by a local reporter.

Later that day:

Dad: *(after answering his mobile)* It's the museum, Paul. It seems your idea of a prehistoric mammal wasn't far off the mark! They want you to interview you on television. Are you interested?

Paul: *(excitedly)* You bet, Dad! Wow! Now this holiday is starting to get interesting!

Examining narrative 2

Use the narrative on page 7 to complete the page.

1. Title

(a) Do you think the title suggests the story?

yes ☐   no ☐

(b) Explain your answer or write an alternative title.

2. Orientation

Answer these questions using the information provided.

Who?

When?

Where?

Why?

3. Complication and events

(a) Why do Paul and Rosa go exploring?

_____

_____

(b) Label the events from 1 to 4 as they occurred.

(i) Paul falls inside the caves. ☐

(ii) Paul and Rosa see some caves. ☐

(iii) Paul and Rosa walk along the beach. ☐

(iv) Paul discovers another chamber in the cave. ☐

4. Resolution

How is the problem of Paul's boredom resolved?

5. Conclusion

Write an extension to the conclusion.

_____

_____

_____

_____

_____

1. Plan a play about a holiday adventure.

Title

Orientation

Complication and events

Resolution

Conclusion

2. Write your narrative as a play script.

3. Edit your work.

The text below has the features indicated.

Title	Costume drama
Orientation – who, when, where, why	The pupils of Wakefield School were busy rehearsing for the end of year play. Today, they were very excited **as** Miss Scott, from the local repertory theatre, was meeting with them after rehearsal to hand out costumes. This would be the first time any of them had worn real theatrical costumes. Usually, mothers were enlisted to help sew **makeshift** costumes, **but** for this performance, the pupils would feel like true professionals. By 5.00 pm, everyone in the cast was dressed.
Complication and significant events – in detail	Katie Summers had the lead role and the most **exquisite** costume. Long after the others had gone home, she was admiring herself in the long mirror and rehearsing her lines. As she heard the cleaners enter the building, she realised the time and hurriedly began to undress. The sound of ripping material made her stomach churn. 'Oh, what have I done?' wailed Katie. As she tried to extricate herself from the mass of silk and satin, she became more entangled. Dragging the heavy dress over her head, her hair caught in the zip. She tried to pull it down so that she could step out of it but the rich garment, **shrouding** her head, would not move. The door opened and Katie heard the sound of cheerful whistling. 'Hello, what have we here?' chuckled Sylvia, pushing her trolley of mops, brushes and dusters. 'Oh Sylvia! Please help me', cried Katie in desperation. 'I'm going to be in so much trouble!' 'Keep still, Katie and stop panicking. I'll set you right.'
Resolution – to the complication	Sylvia's nimble fingers deftly **released** the zip from Katie's hair and the dress dropped to the floor. As Katie picked it up, she **shrieked** in horror at the damage she had caused. There was a long tear down one seam and one side of the zip had been totally ripped from the dress. 'Oh Sylvia! What shall I do? How can I ever fix that!' sighed Katie **despondently**. 'Don't worry, Katie. Leave it with me and I'll have it looking as good as new', comforted Sylvia motherly. 'Oh Sylvia, how can I ever thank you?'
Conclusion – indicating what has changed	The next afternoon, dressed in her splendid costume, Katie and her co-stars had their first dress rehearsal. As Katie came off stage after her final scene, Miss Scott called to her. 'Let me take a look at the dress for a moment, please Katie', she asked in rather a serious tone. Katie trembled as she approached. She had thought Sylvia had done an excellent job, fixing the tears. How would she explain what had happened to Miss Scott? Miss Scott examined the dress closely. 'Remarkable! Quite remarkable! I was sure there was a tear in this dress, a long one, all the way down one seam. How strange!'

- a range of conjunctions to connect text; e.g. **as**, **but**

- varied and interesting adjectives; e.g. **exquisite**, **makeshift**

- descriptive language; e.g. **shrouding**, **despondently**

- verbs in the past tense; e.g. **released**, **shrieked**

- appropriate paragraphing

Teacher information

- Discuss what a narrative is, explaining that it may be presented in many forms; e.g. play, poem, fable.
- Read the narrative on page 11 with the pupils.
- Discuss the different sections of the framework and ensure pupils understand how the text fits into each.
- Emphasise the language features listed to the right of the text above.
- Work through the analysis on page 12 with the pupils.
- Plan a similar narrative, writing ideas for each section within the framework and discuss and model how the plan is transformed into a coherent piece of text.
- Pupils use page 13 to plan and then write a narrative about a mishap involving someone else's property.
- Pupils publish their narratives and illustrate with a series of humorous cartoon sketches. (Publishing)
- Pupils read their work to other groups/classes while others mime the events. (Purpose/Audience)
- Pupils choose three of their cartoon illustrations to enlarge and display with their work. (Display)

Answers

Page 12
1. Teacher check
2. (a) Wakefield School
   (b) pupils and Miss Scott, Katie and Sylvia
   (c) to rehearse a play
   (d) at the end of a school day at the end of the school year.
3. (a) Katie damages a costume
   (b) Removing the costume hastily, Katie tears the zip from the material and the zip gets caught in her hair. The harder she tries to release herself, the more entangled she becomes.
   (c) Teacher check
4. Sylvia, the cleaner, frees Katie's hair from the zip and mends the dress.
5. Teacher check

Costume drama

The pupils of Wakefield School were busy rehearsing for the end of year play. Today, they were very excited as Miss Scott, from the local repertory theatre, was meeting with them after rehearsal to hand out costumes. This would be the first time any of them had worn real theatrical costumes. Usually, mothers were enlisted to help sew makeshift costumes, but for this performance, the pupils would feel like true professionals. By 5.00 pm, everyone in the cast was dressed.

Katie Summers had the lead role and the most exquisite costume. Long after the others had gone home, she was admiring herself in the long mirror and rehearsing her lines. As she heard the cleaners enter the building, she realised the time and hurriedly began to undress. The sound of ripping material made her stomach churn.

'Oh, what have I done?' wailed Katie.

As she tried to extricate herself from the mass of silk and satin, she became more entangled. Dragging the heavy dress over her head, her hair caught in the zip. She tried to pull it down so that she could step out of it but the rich garment, shrouding her head, would not move.

The door opened and Katie heard the sound of cheerful whistling.

'Hello, what have we here?' chuckled Sylvia, pushing her trolley of mops, brushes and dusters.

'Oh Sylvia! Please help me', cried Katie in desperation. 'I'm going to be in so much trouble!'

'Keep still, Katie and stop panicking. I'll set you right.'

Sylvia's nimble fingers deftly released the zip from Katie's hair and the dress dropped to the floor. As Katie picked it up, she shrieked in horror at the damage she had caused. There was a long tear down one seam and one side of the zip had been totally ripped from the dress.

'Oh Sylvia! What shall I do? How can I ever fix that!' sighed Katie despondently.

'Don't worry, Katie. Leave it with me and I'll have it looking as good as new', comforted Sylvia motherly.

'Oh Sylvia, how can I ever thank you?'

The next afternoon, dressed in her splendid costume, Katie and her co-stars had their first dress rehearsal. As Katie came off stage after her final scene, Miss Scott called to her.

'Let me take a look at the dress for a moment, please Katie', she asked in rather a serious tone.

Katie trembled as she approached. She had thought Sylvia had done an excellent job, fixing the tears. How would she explain what had happened to Miss Scott?

Miss Scott examined the dress closely.

'Remarkable! Quite remarkable! I was sure there was a tear in this dress, a long one, all the way down one seam. How strange!'

Examining narrative

Use the narrative on page 11 to complete the page.

1. Title

Explain why the author may have chosen *Costume drama* as a title for this narrative.

2. Orientation

(a) Where is the story set?

(b) Who are the characters?

(c) Why are the characters there?

(d) When does the story take place?

3. Complication and events

(a) What is the complication of the narrative?

_____

_____

_____

(b) Explain briefly how the complication occurred.

(c) Write three interesting adjectives used in the narrative

_____

_____

4. Resolution

Describe how the complication is resolved.

5. Conclusion

Write a different conclusion to the narrative.

_____

_____

_____

_____

_____

_____

_____

Narrative plan ③

1. Plan a narrative about a mishap involving someone else's property.

Title

Orientation

Complication and events

Resolution

Conclusion

2. Write your narrative.

3. Edit your work.

Structural and language features are shown on the left and right of the text below.

Title	**A very strange creature**	• verbs in the past tense; e.g. **saw**, **walked**
Orientation – who, when, where, why	I **saw** the most amazing thing when I **walked** home from training yesterday! Sasha and I had just reached the corner of our street when we saw a crowd of people looking up into the trees along the footpath.	
Events – significant events in detail	We had to stop and find out what was so interesting, so we moved through the crowd until we got close to the front where we had a better view.	• paragraphs to show different sections
	Sitting happily in the branches of one of the trees was the strangest creature I had ever seen! It was only about as big as my school ruler and had a pink face. It had yellow hands and feet. The fur on its back was grey and it had black fur around its mouth and nose. It even had tufts of white fur on its ears! Leaves shook as it scrambled madly backwards and forwards among the branches. Twittering and shrieking noises could be heard coming from behind the leaves.	
	The crowd chatted to each other and pointed at the creature.	• vocabulary to suggest passing of time; e.g. **After about twenty minutes**, **Then**
	Old Mrs Tonkins and Mr Dial carried out a lively discussion about what type of creature it was and whether it was dangerous, while others muttered that Robert needed to be quick about ringing the animal protection board.	
	We all kept our eyes on the creature while we waited, afraid that it might disappear before help could arrive.	
	After about twenty minutes, a truck could be heard coming up the street. We all stepped out of the way and watched two men emerge. They went to the back of the truck and got out a wire cage, a large net and a ladder and harness.	
	The smallest man propped the ladder against the nearest tree and quietly climbed into the lower branches. Once he was seated safely in the fork of the tree, he attached the harness to a strong branch. His partner passed the net up to him and he manoeuvred it until it was over the top of the creature. When he brought it swiftly down, trapping the creature between the net and a tree branch. **Then** he slipped the net underneath and around the creature and handed it down to his partner. He pushed the opening of the net into the cage and released the creature.	
Conclusion – often with an evaluative comment	'It's great that you people saw this little fellow', he stated. 'Someone climbed over the zoo fence last night and let out all the monkeys. We've been collecting them all day. These spider monkeys have only just arrived from South America for our breeding programme. They're the sweetest specimens I've ever seen!'	

Teacher information

- This recount is written in the form of an eyewitness account.
- Allow the pupils to read the recount or choose individual pupils to read selected sections.
- Discuss the recount, asking pupils questions to help them identify the title, orientation, some events and the conclusion.
- Discuss specific language features such as verbs in the past tense, vocabulary to suggest time passing and paragraphs to show separate sections. Pupils should indicate examples of each.
- Allow pupils to complete the analysis on page 16.
- Model the process of planning and writing a recount about a recent school activity such as an assembly or sporting activity. Model writing it as though it were an eyewitness account. Include all language features indicated above.
- Ensure pupils know that the plan is to record ideas only and the actual writing of the recount will come later.
- Pupils use page 17 to plan a recount of an unusual event they have witnessed.
- Pupils write their recounts, which could be included in a class newspaper for display in the school library for other classes to read. (Purpose/Audience/Display)
- A recount of this nature could be written following a discussion about newspapers and communication. Pupils could rewrite newspaper accounts as interesting recounts. (Context)

Answers

Page 16
1-2. Teacher check
3. (a) Teacher check
   (b) Answers will vary but the capture of the monkey is given in great detail.
   (c) Answers will include 'propped', 'climbed', 'was seated', 'attached', 'passed', 'manoeuvred', 'was', 'brought', 'slipped', 'handed', 'pushed' and 'released'.
4. The conclusion tells us that he thinks that the creatures are 'sweet'.

A very strange creature

I saw the most amazing thing when I walked home from training yesterday! Sasha and I had just reached the corner of our street when we saw a crowd of people looking up into the trees along the footpath.

We had to stop and find out what was so interesting, so we moved through the crowd until we got close to the front where we had a better view.

Sitting happily in the branches of one of the trees was the strangest creature I had ever seen! It was only about as big as my school ruler and had a pink face. It had yellow hands and feet. The fur on its back was grey and it had black fur around its mouth and nose. It even had tufts of white fur on its ears! Leaves shook as it scrambled madly backwards and forwards among the branches. Twittering and shrieking noises could be heard coming from behind the leaves.

The crowd chatted to each other and pointed at the creature.

Old Mrs Tonkins and Mr Dial carried out a lively discussion about what type of creature it was and whether it was dangerous, while others muttered that Robert needed to be quick about ringing the animal protection board.

We all kept our eyes on the creature while we waited, afraid that it might disappear before help could arrive.

After about twenty minutes, a truck could be heard coming up the street. We all stepped out of the way and watched two men emerge. They went to the back of the truck and got out a wire cage, a large net and a ladder and harness.

The smallest man propped the ladder against the nearest tree and quietly climbed into the lower branches. Once he was seated safely in the fork of the tree, he attached the harness to a strong branch. His partner passed the net up to him and he manoeuvred it until it was over the top of the creature. When he brought it swiftly down, the creature was trapped between the net and a tree branch. Then he slipped the net underneath and around the creature and handed it down to his partner. He pushed the opening of the net into the cage and released the creature.

'It's great that you people saw this little fellow', he stated. 'Someone climbed over the zoo fence last night and let out all the monkeys. We've been collecting them all day. These spider monkeys have only just arrived from South America for our breeding programme. They're the sweetest specimens I've ever seen!'

Use the recount on page 15 to complete the page.

1. Title

(a) Does this title clearly tell what the recount is about?

yes ☐   no ☐

(b) Write another suitable title.

2. Orientation

Write a brief sentence to substitute for the first paragraph which tells 'who', 'when', 'where', 'why' and 'what'.

_____

_____

_____

_____

3. Events

(a) Use the boxes below to draw and sequence up to six main events which occurred. You may complete your drawings in cartoon form if you wish and include speech bubbles.

(b) Name one event which was described in great detail.

_____

(c) List six different verbs in the past tense in the second last paragraph.

_____

_____

4. Conclusion

What information does the conclusion give us about the man's opinion of the 'strange creatures'?

_____

1. Plan a recount about an unusual event you have witnessed.

Title

Orientation

Who, when, where, why

Events

What things happened?

Conclusion

What happened at the end?

2. Write your recount.

3. Edit your work.

Structural and language features are shown on the left and right of the text below.

Title		
	Email to Dylan	
Orientation – who, when, where, why	Hi Dylan Our plane was late leaving Heathrow on Saturday because of the bad weather. Brad and Lizzie were grumbling and whining **by the time** we finally got on the plane. They're such little kids! Dad was really excited about his new job and Mum was looking forward to finally having a big house and some nice weather. Thank goodness the novelty of being on a plane quietened Brad and Lizzie down for a while **until** we landed in Singapore!	• vocabulary to suggest passing of time; e.g. **by the time**, **until**
Events – significant events in detail	By the time we arrived in Singapore we were all ready to stretch our legs. We spent the night in a really great hotel close to the airport. There was even a telephone in the bathroom! Unfortunately, we had to get up early to get on the plane to Australia. At least I got a window seat on the plane so it wasn't as bad as the first leg of the journey! I got to see 'Kung fu king', but I won't tell you what the film was about and spoil it for you! The food wasn't too bad but I **enjoyed** the chocolate ice-cream the best! I was glad that I filled by backpack with comics and computer games as the trip seemed to go on forever. We were all getting tired of travelling by the time the pilot **announced** that we were making our descent. We finally arrived in Australia on Sunday afternoon. After we had all disembarked and collected our baggage, I was starting to worry again. I realised that it was going to be a big change coming from winter in England to summer in Australia. When we got out of the terminal, we could already feel how hot it was! It's hard to believe it was cold and rainy when we left England. We caught a taxi to the motel where we are staying until our furniture arrives at the new house. Tomorrow, we're taking a hire car to see where we'll be living.	• verbs in the past tense; e.g. **enjoyed**, **announced** • paragraphs to show different sections
Conclusion – often with an evaluative comment	Talk to you soon! Dad wants to use his laptop to email Grandma and Grandpa to let them know we arrived safely! When he's finished, I'm going to ask him how hard it is to learn to ride a surfboard! Your 'mate', Evan!	

Teacher information

- This recount is written in the form of an email. In order to include a number of events, this email is longer than many emails would be.

- Select pupils to read parts or allow pupils to read the recount independently.

- Discuss the recount, asking pupils questions to focus attention on the title, orientation, events and the conclusion.

- Revise the language features which should be included, such as vocabulary to suggest the passing of time and verbs in the past tense.

- Allow the pupils to complete the analysis on page 20, assisting where necessary.

- Ensure that pupils know that the plan on page 21 is to record ideas only and the actual writing of the recount will come later.

- Model the process of completing and using a plan to write a recount in the form of an email. Pupils may like to offer suggestions for a possible title, names of characters, events to include and an interesting comment for the conclusion.

- Pupils may use bullet points with words or sentences to complete their plan (on page 21) of an email describing a recent event to a friend or relative.

- Pupils could type and print their new recount using a computer and display it with a border suggesting an email format. (Publishing/Display)

- Pupils could write their email recount to send to a member of another class at the school to inform them about a recent event. (Purpose/Audience)

- Pupils use their recount in conjunction with a theme about communication or multiculturalism. (Context)

Answers

Page 20

1. Teacher check

2. (a) Teacher check

   (b) Evan's name is at the end of the email.

3. (a) looked out the window (implied), watched a film, ate, read comics, played computer games

   (b) Teacher check

4. 'When he's finished, I'm going to ask him how hard it is to learn to ride a surfboard!'

Email to Dylan

Hi Dylan

Our plane was late leaving Heathrow on Saturday because of the bad weather. Brad and Lizzie were grumbling and whining by the time we finally got on the plane. They're such little kids! Dad was really excited about his new job and Mum was looking forward to finally having a big house and some nice weather. Thank goodness the novelty of being on a plane quietened Brad and Lizzie down for a while until we landed in Singapore!

By the time we arrived in Singapore we were all ready to stretch our legs. We spent the night in a really great hotel close to the airport. There was even a telephone in the bathroom! Unfortunately, we had to get up early to get on the plane to Australia. At least I got a window seat on the plane so it wasn't as bad as the first leg of the journey! I got to see 'Kung fu king', but I won't tell you what the film was about and spoil it for you! The food wasn't too bad but I enjoyed the chocolate ice-cream the best! I was glad that I filled my backpack with comics and computer games as the trip seemed to go on forever. We were all getting tired of travelling by the time the pilot announced that we were making our descent.

We finally arrived in Australia on Sunday afternoon. After we had all disembarked and collected our baggage, I was starting to worry again. I realised that it was going to be a big change coming from winter in England to summer in Australia. When we got out of the terminal, we could already feel how hot it was! It's hard to believe it was cold and rainy when we left England.

We caught a taxi to the motel where we are staying until our furniture arrives at the new house. Tomorrow, we're taking a hire car to see where we'll be living.

Talk to you soon! Dad wants to use his laptop to email Grandma and Grandpa to let them know we arrived safely! When he's finished, I'm going to ask him how hard it is to learn to ride a surfboard!

Your 'mate', Evan!

Use the recount on page 19 to complete the page.

1. Title

Write a new, appropriate
title for the recount.

2. Orientation

An orientation gives the relevant information about 'who', 'when', 'where' and 'why'.

(a) Rewrite the first paragraph as one sentence so that it includes all the information above.

_____

_____

_____

_____

_____

(b) One piece of information was not found in the orientation but at the end. What was it?

_____

_____

4. Conclusion

Which sentence tells that Evan may be feeling a bit more optimistic about the move from England to Australia?

3. Events

(a) List five different things Evan did on the plane. (One is implied!)

(b) Write examples from the text for each of the boxes.

Vocabulary which suggests the passing of time

Verbs in the past tense

1. Plan a recount describing a recent event that you could email to a friend or relative living in another town, city or country. It need not be true!

Title

Orientation

Who, when, where, why

Events

Conclusion

2. Write your recount.

3. Edit your work.

Structural and language features are shown on the left and right of the text below.

Title	The journal of a Chinese gold digger	
Orientation – who, when, where, why	June 1, 1855 Today, we arrived on the goldfields and found our camp. We set up our tent next to the others. We talked to some of the workers and found some who **spoke** the same dialect as us and **discovered** they were from our province.	• verbs in the past tense; e.g. **spoke, discovered**
Events – significant events in detail	June 2,1855 **After** our first meal, we took our tools and headed for the diggings. We found a spot abandoned by the Europeans and started work in our team. It was hard but one of our team saw some chips in the debris so we kept working. June 3, 1855 Some Europeans passed our claims today, yelling and calling out in threatening tones. I was glad that I couldn't understand what they were saying, but I know that they didn't like us being there! **When we got back** to our campsite, some of the tents were collapsed in a heap and cooking utensils and clothes were scattered around in the dirt. I don't understand why they dislike us so much. We are only trying to make a living to look after our families. We don't bother them so why should they bother us? December 14, 1855 Today, I was able to send a small pouch of gold dust back to the trader who gave me the money to come to Australia. The last thing I want is for my family in China to become his slaves. I'm trying to make life better for my family — not worse! It's really hard work to find even a little bit of gold, but I'm used to living in poor conditions and not having very much. I can work as long as I need to. January 20, 1857 The gold seems to be running out now. We have to keep moving to find abandoned sites and to work longer hours for little reward. I have finally repaid my loan and some of my family have joined me. I have come to know this country well. A person can do well for himself if he is prepared to work hard.	• vocabulary to suggest passing of time; e.g. **After, When we got back** • paragraphs to show different sections
Conclusion – often with an evaluative comment	I would like to stay here and make a new life for myself and my family. I'm sure nothing could be as hard as digging for gold but maybe I'll become a rich merchant myself one day!	

Teacher information

• This recount is written in the form of a journal. This particular example doesn't use specific names so the 'who' in the orientation is 'we' and the 'why' is implied.

• Read the recount with the pupils, select pupils to read parts or allow pupils to read the recount independently.

• Discuss the recount, asking questions to help identify the title, the orientation, some events and the conclusion.

• Allow the pupils to complete the analysis on page 24, offering assistance where necessary.

• Ensure that pupils know that the plan is to record ideas only and the actual writing of the recount will come later.

• Model the process of planning and writing a recount if pupils have not completed a plan before. A possible example would be to choose a character from a historical time studied or the recount of a time in the life of a person who comes from another country. Examples such as these will give pupils an understanding of the lives of other people in a different time or culture.

• Pupils may write bullet points in the form of words or sentences to complete their plan on page 25.

• Pupils could write recounts relating to a particular historical time to form the basis of roleplays to perform for the class. (Purpose/Audience)

• Pupils write this recount when completing a theme about the early history of their or another country or multiculturalism. (Context)

• Publish recounts in an 'old-fashioned' font and display with a detailed appropriate sketch or diagram. (Display)

Answers

Page 24

1. Teacher check

2. (a) (i) we

(ii) June 1, 1855

(iii) in our camp, on the goldfields

(b) Teacher check

3. (a) 3

(b) 2

(c) 1

(d) 3

(e) 3

(f) 1

4. This conclusion indicates that the Chinese gold miner may stay in Australia with his family and start a business and become a rich merchant as nothing could be as hard as digging for gold.

The journal of a Chinese gold digger

June 1, 1855

Today, we arrived on the goldfields and found our camp. We set up our tent next to the others. We talked to some of the workers and found some who spoke the same dialect as us and discovered they were from our province.

June 2, 1855

After our first meal, we took our tools and headed for the diggings. We found a spot abandoned by the Europeans and started work in our team. It was hard but one of our team saw some chips in the debris so we kept working.

June 3, 1855

Some Europeans passed our claims today, yelling and calling out in threatening tones. I was glad that I couldn't understand what they were saying, but I know that they didn't like us being there! When we got back to our campsite, some of the tents were collapsed in a heap and cooking utensils and clothes were scattered around in the dirt. I don't understand why they dislike us so much. We are only trying to make a living to look after our families. We don't bother them so why should they bother us?

December 14, 1855

Today, I was able to send a small pouch of gold dust back to the trader who gave me the money to come to Australia. The last thing I want is for my family in China to become his slaves. I'm trying to make life better for my family—not worse! It's really hard work to find even a little bit of gold, but I'm used to living in poor conditions and not having very much. I can work as long as I need to.

January 20, 1857

The gold seems to be running out now. We have to keep moving to find abandoned sites and to work longer hours for little reward. I have finally repaid my loan and some of my family have joined me. I have come to know this country well. The climate is pleasant and a person can do well for himself if he is prepared to work hard.

I would like to stay here and make a new life for myself and my family. I'm sure nothing could be as hard as digging for gold. Maybe I'll become a rich merchant myself one day!

Use the recount on page 23 to complete the page.

1. Title

(a) Tick the boxes.

(i) the title is suitable ☐

(ii) the title supplies extra information ☐

(b) Write another appropriate title.

2. Orientation

(a) Write words from the orientation which show:

(i) **Who?**

(ii) **When?**

(iii) **Where?**

(b) Use the information from the title, the orientation and 'made-up' names to write a sentence for a new orientation.

_____

_____

_____

_____

_____

_____

3. Events

The events in the recount give a vivid description of what life was like for a Chinese gold miner in Australia during the 1850s.

Give the paragraph number of an event which tells:

(a) Chinese gold miners borrowed money to come to Australia. ☐

(b) The Chinese were abused by the European miners. ☐

(c) The Chinese used sites abandoned by the Europeans. ☐

(d) The families of Chinese gold diggers who did not send gold back to repay their loan were taken as slaves by the wealthy traders. ☐

(e) Chinese miners were used to poor conditions, worked hard and were patient. ☐

(f) Chinese gold miners kept to themselves and worked in teams. ☐

4. Conclusion

Many Chinese returned to their homeland after the gold rush. What does the conclusion tell you about this Chinese worker?

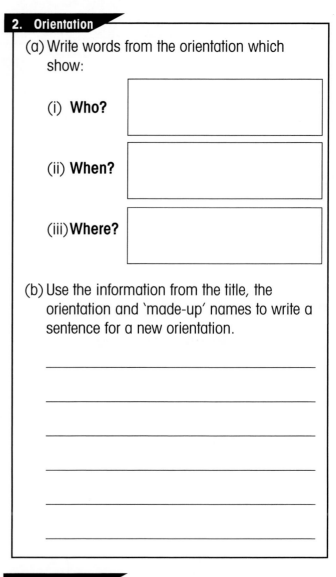

1. Select a character or historical figure from an interesting time you may have studied. Plan a recount in the form of a diary or journal which tells about that person's life.

Title

Orientation

Events

Conclusion

2. Write your recount.

3. Edit your work.

Structural and language features are shown on the left and right of the text below.

Title	Baked lemon and ginger snapper
Goal – the purpose of the procedure	Follow this recipe to create a juicy whole-baked snapper. Serves four.
Materials – the materials required to complete the procedure	Ingredients: • 1 whole snapper (scaled and cleaned) • 2 lemons • 1 tomato • **1 tablespoon grated ginger** • **4 spring onions** • soy sauce (light) • olive oil (light) • dried dill • ground black pepper • salt Utensils: • chopping board • sharp knife • **grater** • measuring spoons • juicer • paper towel • aluminium foil • baking tray
Method – clear in a logical order	Method: 1. Wash fish and pat dry with paper towel. 2. Slice tomato into thick slices. 3. **Slice** one lemon thinly. 4. Chop spring onions evenly. 5. Stuff tomato, half sliced lemon, half spring onions and good pinch of dill inside fish. 6. **Score** each side of fish using sharp knife and rub lightly with olive oil. 7. **Rub** grated ginger evenly on both sides of fish. Press into scores. 8. Make foil 'packet' large enough to hold fish. **Leave** top open and **place** fish inside. 9. Squeeze juice from remaining lemon. Remove pips. 10. Sprinkle fish liberally with lemon juice, soy sauce, salt and pepper. 11. Layer remaining lemon slices and spring onions evenly over top of fish. 12. Close foil packet tightly. 13. Bake on tray in moderate oven at 160 °C – 180 °C for 30 to 35 minutes, depending on size.
Test – an evaluation	Test your lemon and ginger snapper by tasting it!

Right-hand annotations:

- clear concise information—unnecessary words omitted; e.g. **1 tablespoon grated ginger, 4 spring onions**
- subject-specific vocabulary; e.g. **grater, Slice**
- command verbs used in instructions; e.g. **Score, Rub**
- the present tense is used; e.g. **Leave, place**

Teacher information

- Collect a variety of recipe books. Distribute to pupils in small groups and give them the task of finding the 'structure' of a recipe. Groups report back to the class.
- Read the text on page 27 with the class. The text could be enlarged using the accompanying CD on an interactive whiteboard. Discuss each section of the procedure.
- Focus on the language of the text. Note that unnecessary words (such as 'the') are omitted. The steps are written simply and concisely and they are easy to follow.
- The first word of each step in the method of this procedure is a directing verb. These types of verbs are called command verbs (imperatives). Ask pupils for more examples of command verbs.
- Discuss which tense is used in the procedure and ask for pupils to give examples of this. (Present tense)
- Work through the analysis on page 28 with the class.
- Before pupils attempt to plan and write their procedure, model this process to the class. Write a plan for a procedure to make a familiar recipe such as a pitta bread pizza. Emphasise that the first words are often command verbs such as 'Chop', 'Slice' or 'Sprinkle' etc.
- Show the class how to use the plan to write the procedure. It is important to stress that a plan does not contain every word of the written text—just the main points.
- Once the pupils' recipes have been planned and written, they should be proofread and edited. Pupils could publish their recipes using a word processor. Collate the recipes to make a class recipe book. (Publish/Purpose/Audience)
- Choose a recipe to follow and make during a cooking lesson. (Purpose/Context)
- Use a digital camera to take photographs of each step of the new recipe being made. Enlarge the procedure for the recipe to A3 and attach the photographs to each step. Discuss sequencing with the class. (Display/Publish/Context)
- If funds are available for the ingredients, pupils make their own recipes. Food could be sold to other pupils as a class fundraiser. (Purpose/Audience)

Answers

Page 28

1. Teacher check
2. to make baked lemon and ginger snapper
3. Teacher check
4. (a) Teacher check
   (b) Answers will vary
   (c) If the steps are not followed in the correct order, the procedure will not work.
5. The snapper will be cooked and tasty.

Baked lemon and ginger snapper

Follow this recipe to create a juicy whole-baked snapper. Serves four.

Ingredients:

- 1 whole snapper (scaled and cleaned)
- 2 lemons
- 1 tomato
- 1 tablespoon grated ginger
- 4 spring onions
- soy sauce (light)
- olive oil (light)
- dried dill
- ground black pepper
- salt

Utensils:

- chopping board
- sharp knife
- grater
- measuring spoons
- juicer
- paper towel
- aluminium foil
- baking tray

Method:

1. Wash fish and pat dry with paper towel.
2. Slice tomato into thick slices.
3. Slice one lemon thinly.
4. Chop spring onions evenly.
5. Stuff tomato, half sliced lemon, half spring onions and good pinch of dill inside fish.
6. Score each side of fish using sharp knife and rub lightly with olive oil.
7. Rub grated ginger evenly on both sides of fish. Press into scores.
8. Make foil 'packet' large enough to hold fish. Leave top open and place fish inside.
9. Squeeze juice from remaining lemon. Remove pips.
10. Sprinkle fish liberally with lemon juice, soy sauce, salt and pepper.
11. Layer remaining lemon slices and spring onions evenly over top of fish.
12. Close foil packet tightly.
13. Bake in moderate oven at 160 °C – 180 °C for 30 to 35 minutes, depending on size.

Test your lemon and ginger snapper by tasting it!

Use the procedure on page 27 to complete the page.

1. Title

(a) Is the title of the procedure appropriate?

yes ☐   no ☐

(b) Write an alternative title which would suit this procedure.

2. Goal

What is the goal of this procedure?

_____

_____

3. Ingredients

Procedures are written using clear, concise information. Unnecessary words are not included.

Choose two examples from the list of ingredients that show this.

_____

_____

4. Method

(a) Use the boxes below to draw three of the main steps from the method. Write the step number in the box.

(b) Do you think the procedure would be easier to follow if diagrams were included?   **yes** ☐ **no** ☐

Explain _____

_____

(c) Explain why the order of the steps is important. _____

_____

5. Test

How will you know if the recipe is a success?

_____

1. Plan a procedure for a recipe you know.

Title

Goal

Objective of procedure

Ingredients

Utensils

Method

Concisely written, numbered steps in order.

Test

How will you test if the recipe is successful?

2. Write your procedure.

3. Edit your work.

Structural and language features are shown on the left and right of the text below.

Title	Salty-dough ladybirds
Goal – the purpose of the procedure	Make salty-dough ladybirds to give as gifts.

• clear concise information—unnecessary words omitted; e.g. **2 cups flour, 1 cup water**

Materials – the materials required to complete the procedure	What you need: • **1 cup water** • toothpick • ribbons • 1 cup salt • pencil • baking paper • **2 cups flour** • clear acrylic sealer • oven mitts • paintbrushes—medium and fine • baking tray • cellophane paper • acrylic paint—red, black and white • bowl • cup

• subject-specific vocabulary; e.g. **Preheat oven, 7 centimetres long**

Method – clear in a logical order	What to do 1. **Preheat oven** to 120° Celsius. 2. Mix flour, salt and water until dough is formed. 3. Knead dough on floured surface until mixture becomes smooth and feels elastic. Note: If dough is sticky, sprinkle more flour onto it, but not too much as dough will dry out and crack. 4. Roll small handfuls of dough into egg-shaped ovals about **7 centimetres** long with rounded backs and flat bases. 5. Draw line to two-thirds of way down centre of dough using pencil. Line should be half a centimetre deep. 6. **Mark** a 'V' shape where line ends, using pencil. This makes ladybird's head. 7. **Create** spots by poking pencil half a centimetre deep into back of ladybird. 8. Repeat steps 5 to 7 for all pieces of dough. 9. Line tray with baking paper. 10. Place ladybirds on tray and **bake** for approximately 2 to 2.5 hours. 11. Remove tray from oven using oven mitts. Allow to cool overnight. 12. Paint ladybirds' bodies red and heads black. 13. Use toothpick (or fine paintbrush) to paint ladybirds' spots and line between wings black. Allow to dry. 14. Paint two eyes with white paint using toothpick. When dry, carefully paint black centre of eyes using toothpick. 15. Complete ladybirds with coat of clear acrylic sealer. Allow to dry. 16. Wrap ladybirds in cellophane and **tie** with ribbons.

• command verbs used in instructions; e.g. **Mark, Create**

• the present tense is used; e.g. **bake, tie**

Test – an evaluation	Ladybirds should be completely dry, hard and painted correctly.

Teacher information

• Ask pupils to think of objects they have made by following instructions such as models, construction toys, craft items etc. What is usually included in the instructions?

• Read the text on page 31 with the class. The text could be enlarged using the accompanying CD on an interactive whiteboard. Discuss each section of the procedure.

• Focus on the language of the text. Note that unnecessary words (such as 'the') are omitted. The steps are written simply and clearly and are easy to follow.

• The first word of each step in the method of this procedure is a verb that is a direct instruction—these types of verbs are called command verbs. Ask pupils for more examples of command verbs.

• Discuss which tense is being used in the procedure and ask for pupils to give examples of this. (Present tense)

• Work through the analysis on page 32 with the class.

• Before pupils attempt to plan and write their procedure, model this process to the class. Write a plan for a procedure to make a simple craft item such as a snowman from modelling clay and other household materials.

• Show the class how to use the plan to write the procedure. It is important to stress that a plan does not contain every word of the written text—just the main points.

• Once the pupils' procedures for 'salty-dough' animals have been planned and written, they should be proofread and edited. Pupils could publish their procedures using a word processor. Collate the procedures to make a class craft book. (Publish/Purpose/Audience)

• Choose one pupil's procedure to follow and make with the class. Use a digital camera to photograph the pupils making the craft items and display. (Purpose/Display)

• Organise for pupils to give their procedures to pupils in younger classes, who must follow them precisely. Did the finished products look as the writers intended? Why/Why not? Analyse procedures to find where instructions were not clear. (Purpose)

Answers

Page 32

1. (a) Teacher check

2. make salty-dough ladybirds to give as gifts

3. (a) Yes

   (b) The materials come before the method so the reader can collect the items required before beginning the procedure.

4. (a) Teacher check

   (b) Answers should include the first words from the steps in the 'What to do' section.

   (c) Teacher check

   (d) Line tray with baking paper.

5. (a) Ladybirds are dry.   (b) Ladybirds are hard.

   (c) Ladybirds have been painted correctly.

Salty-dough ladybirds.......................

Goal: Make salty-dough ladybirds to give as gifts.

What you need:

- 1 cup water
- 1 cup salt
- 2 cups flour
- paintbrushes—medium and fine
- acrylic paint—red, black and white

- toothpicks
- pencil
- clear acrylic sealer
- baking tray
- bowl

- ribbons
- baking paper
- oven mitts
- cellophane paper
- cup

What to do

1. Preheat oven to 120 °C.
2. Mix flour, salt and water until dough is formed.
3. Knead dough on floured surface until mixture becomes smooth and feels elastic.
   Note: If dough is sticky, sprinkle more flour onto it, but not too much as dough will dry out and crack.
4. Roll small handfuls of dough into egg-shaped ovals about 7 centimetres long with rounded backs and flat bases.
5. Draw line to two-thirds of way down centre of dough using pencil. Line should be half a centimetre deep.
6. Mark a 'V' shape where line ends, using pencil. This makes ladybird's head.
7. Create spots by poking pencil half a centimetre deep into back of ladybird.
8. Repeat steps 5 to 7 for all pieces of dough.
9. Line tray with baking paper.
10. Place ladybirds on tray and bake for approximately 2 to 2.5 hours.
11. Remove tray from oven using oven mitts. Allow to cool overnight.
12. Paint ladybirds' bodies red and heads black.
13. Use toothpick (or fine paintbrush) to paint ladybirds' spots and line between wings black. Allow to dry.
14. Paint two eyes with white paint using toothpick. When dry, carefully paint black centre of eyes using toothpick.
15. Complete ladybirds with coat of clear acrylic sealer. Allow to dry.
16. Wrap ladybirds in cellophane and tie with ribbons.

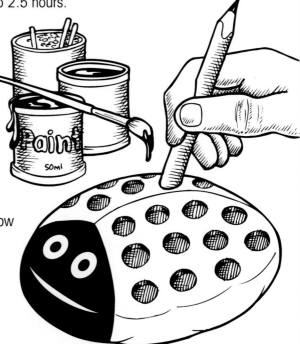

Ladybirds should be completely dry, hard and painted correctly.

Use the procedure on page 31 to complete the page.

1. Title

(a) Does the title clearly tell what the procedure is about? **yes** ☐ **no** ☐

(b) Write another suitable title.

2. Goal

The goal of the procedure is to

_____

_____

_____

3. What you need

(a) The materials are set out as lists using bullet points. **yes** ☐ **no** ☐

(b) Why are the materials and utensils listed before the method?

_____

_____

4. Steps

(a) Do you think a diagram for some of the steps of the procedure would be useful? **yes** ☐ **no** ☐

Explain _____

_____

(b) The first word in instructions is often a directing verb called a 'command' verb. Write examples of command verbs from the text.

(c) List three more examples of command verbs not found in the text.

_____ label _____ _____

(d) Procedures are written clearly so they can be easily followed. Unnecessary words are not included. Rewrite this sentence removing all unnecessary words.

Then you should line the tray with some of the baking paper you prepared.

_____

5. Test

List three ways you will know if the procedure has been followed correctly.

_____

_____

_____

Procedure plan 2

1. Plan a procedure for making a different kind of 'salty-dough' animal. Practise making your animal first using modelling clay.

Title

Goal

What you need

What to do (Method)

Concisely written, numbered steps.

Test

How will you test if the procedure is a success?

2. Write your procedure.

3. Edit your work.

Structural and language features are shown on the left and right of the text below.

Title	**Battleships!**
Goal – the purpose of the procedure	Locate and destroy the enemy's fleet.
Materials – the materials required to complete the procedure	Materials: • pencil • ruler • red pencil • **yellow pencil** • 4 sheets of grid paper (usually square)—two per player Note: 'Battleships' is a game for two players.
Method – clear in a logical order	Instructions: 1. Grid paper represents the ocean in which each player's **fleet** of 15 ships is hiding. 2. **Number** each square vertically up left side of grid paper, on both sheets of paper. Begin with '1' at the bottom and **write numbers near centre** of squares. 3. Write letters **horizontally**, left to right, across bottom of both sheets of paper. Begin at 'A' and write letters near centre of squares. Squares can now be identified by letter and number coordinates; e.g. A6. 4. **Label** one grid 'My ships' and the other 'My shots'. 5. Players secretly outline each ship of their fleet of 15 ships on their 'My ships' grid. Ships occupy a specified number of squares (see below) and may be drawn horizontally or vertically but not diagonally. No two ships can occupy the same grid square. Number and size of ships in each fleet 1 carrier 5 squares in length (5 x 1) 4 destroyers each 2 squares in length (2 x 1) 2 battleships each 4 squares in length (4 x 1) 5 submarines each 1 square long (1 x 1) 3 cruisers each 3 squares in length (3 x 1) 6. The first player begins by naming a coordinate; e.g. F5. If opposing player has a ship on that coordinate, he/she says 'hit' and colours that square on the 'My ships' page red; if not he/she says 'miss' and colours the square yellow. The first player uses the same code to colour that square; e.g. F5 red or yellow on his/her 'My shots' sheet. 7. Second player then names a coordinate. Opposition declares 'hit' or 'miss' and both players colour their sheets accordingly. 8. When a ship is coloured completely, the owner must **declare** it sunk. 9. Game continues until one player **sinks** all the opposing player's ships.
Test – an evaluation	The winner is the player with ships remaining.

Right margin notes:
- clear concise information—unnecessary words omitted; e.g. **yellow pencil**, **write numbers near centre**
- subject-specific vocabulary; e.g. **horizontally**, **fleet**
- command verbs used in instructions; e.g. **Number**, **Label**
- the present tense is used; e.g. **declare**, **sinks**

Teacher information

- Ask pupils to think of games they have played using instructions to help them with the rules; for example, board games. What is usually included in these instructions?
- Read the text on page 35 with the class. The text could be enlarged using the accompanying CD on an interactive whiteboard. Discuss each section of the procedure.
- Focus on the language of the text. Note that unnecessary words (such as 'the') are omitted. The steps are written simply and clearly and are easy to follow.
- The first word of many steps in the method is a verb that is a direct instruction—these types of verbs are called command verbs. Ask pupils for more examples of command verbs (imperatives).
- Discuss which tense is being used in the procedure and ask for pupils to give examples of this. (Present tense)
- Work through the analysis on page 36 with the class.
- Before pupils attempt to plan and write their procedure, model this process to the class. Write a plan for a procedure to play a simple pencil and paper game such as hangman or noughts and crosses.
- Show the class how to use the plan to write the procedure. It is important to stress that a plan does not contain every word of the written text—just the main points.
- Pupils plan, write and edit their procedures.

- Pupils publish their game procedures using a word processor or neat handwriting. Artwork can be included. The games can be collated to form a class book of games. (Publish/Display)
- Pupils give their game procedure to a group in the same class or another class to play. The group must follow the instructions precisely. The players offer feedback to the author with suggestions for making the instructions clearer. (Audience/Purpose)

Answers

Page 36

1. (a) Battleships
   (b) Answers will vary
2. The goal is to locate and destroy the enemy's fleet.
3. If an item is left off the materials list, the reader will be unable to follow the procedure to play the game.
4. (a) Number, Write, Label, Begin
   (b) Teacher check
   (c) The steps are numbered to show the reader that they must be followed in order.
   (d) If the steps are not followed in the correct order, the procedure will not work.
5. Locate and destroy the enemy's fleet.

Battleships!

Locate and destroy the enemy's fleet.

Materials:

- pencil
- ruler
- 4 sheets of grid paper (usually square)—two per player
- red pencil
- yellow pencil

Note: 'Battleships' is a game for two players.

Instructions:

1. Grid paper represents the ocean in which each player's fleet of 15 ships is hiding.
2. Number each square vertically up left side of grid paper, on both sheets of paper. Begin with '1' at the bottom and write numbers near centre of squares.
3. Write letters horizontally, left to right, across bottom of both sheets of paper. Begin at 'A' and write letters near centre of squares. Squares can now be identified by letter and number coordinates; e.g. A6.
4. Label one grid 'My ships' and the other 'My shots'.
5. Players secretly outline each ship of their fleet of 15 ships on their 'My ships' grid. Ships occupy a specified number of squares (see below) and may be drawn horizontally or vertically but not diagonally. No two ships can occupy the same grid square.

Number and size of ships in each fleet

1 carrier	5 squares in length (5 x 1)
4 destroyers	each 2 squares in length (2 x 1)
2 battleships	each 4 squares in length (4 x 1)
5 submarines	each 1 square long (1 x 1)
3 cruisers	each 3 squares in length (3 x 1)

6. The first player begins by naming a coordinate; e.g. F5. If opposing player has a ship on that coordinate, he/she says 'hit' and colours that square on the 'My ships' page red; if not he/she says 'miss' and colours the square yellow. The first player uses the same code to colour that square; e.g. F5 red or yellow on his/her 'My shots' sheet.
7. Second player then names a coordinate. Opposition declares 'hit' or 'miss' and both players colour their sheets accordingly.
8. When a ship is coloured completely, the owner must declare it sunk.
9. Game continues until one player sinks all the opposing player's ships.

The winner is the player with ships remaining.

Use the procedure on page 35 to complete the page.

1. Title

(a) The title of this procedure is

_____

(b) Write another suitable title.

_____

2. Goal

What is the goal of this procedure?

_____

_____

_____

3. Materials

What would happen if something needed was left off the list of materials required?

_____

_____

4. Instructions

(a) Often the first word of step in the instructions is a directing verb called a command verb. Colour the command verbs from the list of first words below.

Squares	Number	Write	Label	Grid
Players	Begin	Second	When	Game

(b) List four more present tense verbs from the procedure.

    occupy   _____ _____ _____ _____

(c) Why are the steps in the method numbered?

_____

_____

_____

_____

(d) Explain why the order of the steps is important.

_____

_____

_____

_____

5. Test

What does the winner of the game need to do?

_____

_____

_____

1. Plan a procedure for playing a game you know well. It may be a pencil and paper game, a board game or a game played outside.

Title

Goal

Materials

Procedure

Numbered, concisely written steps.

Test

How will you know if the game has been played successfully?

2. Write your procedure.

3. Edit your work.

Structural and language features are shown on the left and right of the text below.

Title	**Problems with plastic**
Classification – a general statement about the subject of the report	It **is estimated** that 500 billion to 1 trillion plastic bags are now made and used each year. Waste plastic, particularly in the form of used plastic shopping bags, **causes** immense problems worldwide for both land and marine environments.
Description – provides accurate description and facts	The problems they cause in the environment include blocking drainage systems, creating litter, adding to **landfill waste**, choking marine life and consuming energy during the manufacturing process.
	Most plastic bags are made from **high density polyethylene** (HDPE). HDPE is made from liquefied petroleum gas (LPG). The amount of LPG needed to make one plastic bag would drive a car about 100 metres. An enormous amount of LPG is used to make the amount of plastic bags the world requires.
	Plastic bags decompose at an incredibly slow rate, **ranging from 20 to 1000 years**. This means that plastic bags **are continuing to accumulate**. They may be reused or recycled, but are not being destroyed.
	On land, plastic bags block drains and gutters, stopping the flow of rainwater and sewage, resulting in pollution and threatening natural environments. Land animals can eat or become trapped in plastic bags. When the animals die, their bodies naturally decompose at a much quicker rate than the bag. The plastic the animal swallowed remains in the environment to be swallowed by another animal.
	Scientists believe more than 100 000 marine mammals such as seals, whales and dolphins die each year after being tangled in waste plastic. The plastic becomes twisted around the animals' limbs or fins, cutting into their flesh. This slows them down so they find it difficult to catch or eat food and makes them easy prey. Turtles are thought to mistake floating plastic bags for jellyfish, their favourite food. **The plastic** can choke the turtle or block its stomach so **it** cannot eat.
	Birds are attracted to the bright colour of some plastics and eat them. This can choke or poison the birds. Dead chicks have been found to have plastic in their stomachs. The parents had been feeding them what they thought was food.
Conclusion – a final comment about the subject of the report. (It may include a personal comment by the writer.)	People can help solve this problem in the following ways. They can reduce the use of plastic bags by using paper or cloth bags, and reuse and recycle plastic bags as much as possible. People also need to remember that plastic bags put in bins will eventually end up in landfill, potentially at large in the environment.

Right-hand language features:
- written in timeless present tense; e.g. **is estimated, causes**
- technical vocabulary and subject-specific terms are used; e.g. **landfill waste, high density polyethylene**
- uses factual language rather than imaginative; e.g. **ranging from 20 to 1000 years, are continuing to accumulate**
- written in the third person; e.g. **The plastic, it**
- information is organised into paragraphs

Teacher information

- Read through the information report with the pupils and discuss the features of a report.
- Work through the analysis on page 40 with the class.

   Explain that: 'I', 'we', 'my' and 'our' are examples of the **first person**

   'you' and 'your' are examples of the **second person**

   'he', 'she', 'it' and 'they' are examples of the **third person**

   For example: I/We take my/our dog for a walk every morning. (first person)

   You take your dog for a walk every morning. (second person)

   Gemma/She takes her dog for a walk every morning./They take their/the dog for a walk every morning. (third person)

- Before pupils attempt to plan and write their own information report on page 41, model this process with the whole class, using another issue pupils are familiar with. Pupils will need to have gathered sufficient information about the subject of their choice prior to planning their report.
- Pupils' reports could be read out orally by them in small groups or to the whole class and discussed. (Purpose/Audience)

- Published reports, accompanied with appropriate illustrations or photographs, could be displayed for other pupils to read and compare. (Publishing/Display/Purpose)
- The activity could be done in conjunction with a science, health or geography topic. (Context/Purpose)

Answers

Page 40

1. (a) Problems with plastic
   (b) Teacher check
2. Teacher check
3. (a) (i) high density polyethylene
      (ii) liquefied petroleum gas
   (b) Answers will vary but should reflect the following:

      Paragraph 3 – The number of plastic bags continues to accumulate, as they decompose at a very slow rate.

      Paragraph 5 – It describes the effects plastic bags have on marine life.
   (c) block, stopping, resulting, threatening
   (d) Birds are attracted to the bright colours of some plastics and if they eat them they can choke or be poisoned.
4. Plastic bags put in bins will eventually end up in landfill, potentially at large in the environment.

Problems with plastic

It is estimated that 500 billion to 1 trillion plastic bags are now made and used each year. Waste plastic, particularly in the form of used plastic shopping bags, causes immense problems worldwide for both land and marine environments.

The problems they cause in the environment include blocking drainage systems, creating litter, adding to landfill waste, choking marine life and consuming energy during the manufacturing process.

Most plastic bags are made from high density polyethylene (HDPE). HDPE is made from liquefied petroleum gas (LPG). The amount of LPG needed to make one plastic bag would drive a car about 100 metres. An enormous amount of LPG is used to make the amount of plastic bags the world requires.

Plastic bags decompose at a very slow rate, ranging from 20 to 1000 years. This means that plastic bags are continuing to accumulate. They may be reused or recycled, but are not being destroyed.

On land, plastic bags block drains and gutters, stopping the flow of rainwater and sewage, resulting in pollution and threatening natural environments. Land animals can eat or become trapped in plastic bags. When the animals die, their bodies naturally decompose at a much quicker rate than the bag.

The plastic the animal swallowed remains in the environment to be swallowed by another animal.

Scientists believe more than 100 000 marine mammals such as seals, whales and dolphins die each year after being tangled in waste plastic. The plastic becomes twisted around the animals' limbs or fins, cutting into their flesh. This slows them down so they find it difficult to catch or eat food and makes them easy prey. Turtles are thought to mistake floating plastic bags for jellyfish, their favourite food. The plastic can choke the turtle or block its stomach so it cannot eat.

Birds are attracted to the bright colour of some plastics and eat them. This can choke or poison the birds. Dead chicks have been found to have plastic in their stomachs. The parents had been feeding them what they thought was food.

People can help solve this problem in the following ways. They can reduce the use of plastic bags by using paper or cloth bags, and reuse and recycle plastic bags as much as possible. People also need to remember that plastic bags put in bins will eventually end up in landfill, potentially at large in the environment.

Use the report on page 39 to complete the page.

1. Title

(a) The title of this information report is

_____

(b) Why do you think this title was chosen?

_____

_____

_____

_____

2. Classification

List two facts from this section.

_____

_____

3. Description

(a) What technical words do these letters stand for?

(i) HDPE _____

_____

(ii) LPG _____

_____

(b) What is the main idea of each of these paragraphs in the description section?

Paragraph 3

Paragraph 5

(c) Highlight the present tense verbs in this sentence.

On land, plastic bags block drains and gutters, stopping the flow of rainwater and sewage, resulting in pollution and threatening natural environments.

(d) Name an animal and use pronouns such as 'it' or 'they' to change this sentence from the **first** person to the **third** person.

We are attracted to the bright colours of some plastics and if we eat them we can choke or be poisoned.

_____

_____

_____

_____

4. Conclusion

What important point does the writer want people to remember?

1. Plan an information report on an issue you have learnt about in geography, science or health. Remember to include accurate facts and use vocabulary suited to your subject.

Title

Classification

A general statement about the subject.

Description

Divide the description into sections.

Conclusion

It may contain a personal opinion.

2. Write your report.

3. Edit your work.

Structural and language features are shown on the left and right of the text below.

Title	**The circulatory system**
Classification – a general statement about the subject of the report	The human circulatory system **is made up** of the heart, the blood vessels and the blood.
Description – provides accurate description and facts	The heart is the centre of the circulatory system. It **is a muscular, pear-shaped organ** about the size of a closed fist, with four chambers **separated by valves**. The sound heard through a stethoscope is these heart valves closing. Two pumps, side by side, continually **send** blood around the body.

The blood vessels are a series of connecting tubes throughout the body. If the network of these vessels through which blood flows was stretched end to end it would be more than 100 000 kilometres in length. The strongest of all the vessels are **the arteries**, which carry blood from the heart to the tissues and organs like the brain, kidney and liver. **They** must withstand the pressure of the blood as it surges from the heart after each beat. Arteries appear red because they carry blood with oxygen.

Veins carry blood back to the heart and are much thinner than arteries because the blood flows through at a lower pressure. They appear blue as they are carrying blood without oxygen back to the heart.

As arteries get further away from the heart, they become smaller and divide into arterioles and further divide into capillaries. These connect arteries to veins. Capillaries are extremely tiny vessels that carry blood to and from every cell in the body. The walls are so thin that oxygen and nutrients can pass through them into the cells and waste products and carbon dioxide pass back through the walls into the bloodstream.

Besides delivering oxygen and nutrients to the cells and helping dispose of waste products and carbon dioxide, the circulatory system performs other functions. White blood cells destroy **bacteria** and **viruses**, helping to protect the body from disease. Circulating blood is directed to and from vessels in the skin to help increase or decrease body temperature. Blood also carries hormones which affect or control activities in the body. |
| **Conclusion –** a final comment about the subject of the report. (It may include a personal comment by the writer.) | The human circulatory system performs many vital functions, so it is important that it is not damaged by disease or injury. Adequate exercise, a healthy diet and regular medical check-ups are the main factors in keeping this system working efficiently. |

- written in timeless present tense; e.g. **is made up**, **send**

- uses factual language rather than imaginative; e.g. **is a muscular, pear-shaped organ**, **separated by valves**

- written in the third person; e.g. **the arteries, They**

- technical vocabulary and subject-specific terms are used; e.g. **bacteria, viruses**

- information is organised into paragraphs

Teacher information

- Read through the scientific report with the pupils and discuss the features of a report.

- Revise the third person (see page 38). Pupils complete the analysis on page 44.

- Before pupils attempt to plan and write their own scientific report on page 45, model this process with the whole class, using another scientific subject they are familiar with. Pupils will need to have gathered information about the subject of their choice prior to planning their report.

- Pupils' reports could be read out orally by them in small groups or to the whole class and discussed. (Purpose/ Audience)

- Published reports, accompanied with appropriate illustrations, could be displayed for other pupils to read and compare. (Publishing/Display/Purpose)

- The activity could be done in conjunction with a health and values unit. (Context)

Answers

Page 44

1. (a) The circulatory system
   (b) Teacher check

2. The circulatory system is made up of the heart, blood vessels and blood.

3. (a) Teacher check
   (b) are, flows, appear, are carrying
   (c) As arteries get further away from the heart, they become smaller and divide into arterioles.

4. (a) adequate exercise, a healthy diet and regular medical check-ups

The circulatory system

The human circulatory system is made up of the heart, the blood vessels and the blood.

The heart is the centre of the circulatory system. It is a muscular, pear-shaped organ about the size of a closed fist, with four chambers separated by valves. The sound heard through a stethoscope is these heart valves closing. Two pumps, side by side, continually send blood around the body.

The blood vessels are a series of connecting tubes throughout the body. If the network of these vessels through which blood flows was stretched end to end it would be more than 100 000 kilometres in length. The strongest of all the vessels are the arteries, which carry blood from the heart to the tissues and organs like the brain, kidney and liver. They must withstand the pressure of the blood as it surges from the heart after each beat. Arteries appear red because they carry blood with oxygen.

Veins carry blood back to the heart and are much thinner than arteries because the blood flows through at a lower pressure. They appear blue as they are carrying blood without oxygen back to the heart.

As arteries get further away from the heart, they become smaller and divide into arterioles and further divide into capillaries. These connect arteries to veins. Capillaries are extremely tiny vessels that carry blood to and from every cell in the body. The walls are so thin that oxygen and nutrients can pass through them into the cells and waste products and carbon dioxide pass back through the walls into the bloodstream.

Besides delivering oxygen and nutrients to the cells and helping dispose of waste products and carbon dioxide, the circulatory system performs other functions. White blood cells destroy bacteria and viruses, helping to protect the body from disease. Circulating blood is directed to and from vessels in the skin to help increase or decrease body temperature. Blood also carries hormones which affect or control activities in the body.

The human circulatory system performs many vital functions, so it is important that it is not damaged by disease or injury. Adequate exercise, a healthy diet and regular medical check-ups are the main factors in keeping this system working efficiently.

lung

heart

liver

stomach

kidney

capillary bed

intestine

vein

artery

Use the report on page 43 to complete the page.

1. Title

(a) The title of this scientific report is

_____

(b) Write another suitable title.

2. Classification

What information is given in the classification?

3. Description

(a) Write keywords and phrases from the report to describe the appearance and function of each of these parts of the body.

heart	artery	vein	capillary

(b) List four more present tense verbs from paragraph 3 of the description section.

___carry___ _____ _____ _____ _____

(c) This sentence about arteries has been written in the first person. Change it so it is in the third person.

As we get further away from the heart, we become smaller and divide into arterioles.

_____

_____

4. Conclusion

What suggestions does the writer give for keeping the circulatory system working efficiently?

1. Plan a scientific report about a healthy diet.
   Remember to use scientific wording and include accurate facts.

Title

Classification

A general statement about the subject.

Description

Divide the description into sections; e.g. how to achieve it, why it is important and how it helps.

Conclusion

It may contain a personal opinion.

2. Write your report.   3. Edit your work.

Structural and language features are shown on the left and right of the text below.

Title– the headline states what is being reported	**The TRAVELLERS GUIDE** **8 March** **ANTARCTIC EXPERIENCE**	• written in the third person; e.g. **Antarctica, It**
Classification – a general statement about the subject of the report	**Antarctica** is unlike any other place on Earth. **It** is the coldest, windiest, driest and highest (on average) continent. Yet this inhospitable place is considered by travellers as being one of the most beautiful places to visit, particularly the Antarctic Peninsula.	• written in timeless present tense; e.g. **is circular, extending**
Description – provides accurate description and facts	Antarctica is roughly **circular** in shape, with a long 'arm' known as the Antarctic Peninsula **extending** towards South America. The peninsula is the most **densely populated** region of the continent, containing a scattering of research posts and their personnel. The area is more hospitable with a 'warmer' climate due to its northerly location and the influence of the surrounding ocean, and therefore has the most wildlife to study. **More than 13 000 tourists** visit Antarctica each year on commercial ships and private yachts. Some of these are sightseeing tours only, without landings. Any landings are carefully monitored according to strict guidelines to protect the environment, with no more than 100 people at a time going ashore. Antarctica's attractions include viewing and photographing a white, clean, pure environment with pack ice, giant icebergs and glaciers; visits to penguin colonies; expeditions to explorers' historical huts; discovering how scientists live and work in Antarctica for extended periods; whale sightings; and looking at the variety of seals and bird life. A tour by ship of the Antarctic Peninsula has another attraction. Deception Island, located off the northern tip of the peninsula, was formed by a volcano. Its collapsed volcanic cone, called a 'caldera', provides one of the world's safest natural harbours. The volcano is still active, with the most recent eruptions occurring in 1991–1992. The volcanic activity forces hot water up through narrow **fissures** along the shore at a place called Pendulum Cove. The water is not deep enough for swimming but bathing in the **thermally heated waters** surrounded by ice makes it a popular tourist attraction. Most cruises to the Antarctic Peninsula leave from the relatively nearby port of Ushuaia in Argentina, between the warmer months of November and March when the winter pack ice breaks up.	• uses factual language rather than imaginative; e.g. **densely populated, More than 13 000 tourists** • technical vocabulary and subject-specific terms are used; e.g. **thermally heated waters, fissures** • information is organised into paragraphs
Conclusion – a final comment about the subject of the report. (It may include an expert or personal opinion or be a summarising comment.)	A visit to this unique and fascinating place is an experience unlike anywhere else on the planet. Juan Rodriguez, Argentina	

Teacher information

• Read through the magazine travel report with the pupils and discuss its features.

• Revise the third person (see page 38). Pupils complete the analysis on page 48.

• Before pupils attempt to plan and write their own report on page 49, model this process with the whole class, using another place of interest pupils have studied in class or are familiar with. Pupils will need to have gathered information about the place of their choice prior to planning their report.

• Pupils' reports could be read out orally by them in small groups or to the whole class and discussed. (Purpose/Audience)

• Published reports, accompanied by appropriate illustrations, could be displayed for other pupils to read and compare. (Publishing/Display/Purpose)

• The activity could be done in conjunction with a geography topic. (Context/Purpose)

Answers

Page 48

1. (a) Antarctic experience
   (b) Teacher check

2. Answers should include four of the following: unlike, coldest, windiest, driest, highest, inhospitable, beautiful

3. (a) The answer should reflect that it lists some of Antarctica's tourist attractions.
   (b) (i) caldera
       (ii) fissure
   (c) Answers should include five of the following: include, viewing, photographing, discovering, live, work, looking
   (d) Possible answers include:
       (i) Antarctica/It is roughly circular in shape its peninsula is its most populated region.
       (ii) Antarctica/It is one of the best places people can visit.
       (iii) People/ Tourists/ Everyone should visit Antarctica.

4. (a) He says it is a unique and fascinating place and an experience unlike anywhere else on the planet.
   (b) Teacher check

The Traveller's Guide

8 March

ANTARCTIC EXPERIENCE

Bathers at Pendulum Cove, Deception Island

Antarctica is unlike any other place on Earth. It is the coldest, windiest, driest and highest (on average) continent. Yet this inhospitable place is considered by travellers as being one of the most beautiful places to visit, particularly the Antarctic Peninsula.

Antarctica is roughly circular in shape, with a long 'arm' known as the Antarctic Peninsula extending towards South America. The peninsula is the most densely populated region of the continent, containing a scattering of research posts and their personnel. The area is more hospitable with a 'warmer' climate due to its northerly location and the influence of the surrounding ocean, and therefore has the most wildlife to study.

More than 13 000 tourists visit Antarctica each year on commercial ships and private yachts. Some of these are sightseeing tours only, without landings. Any landings are carefully monitored according to strict guidelines to protect the environment, with no more than 100 people at a time going ashore.

Antarctica's attractions include viewing and photographing a white, clean, pure environment with pack ice, giant icebergs and glaciers; visits to penguin colonies; expeditions to explorers' historical huts; discovering how scientists live and work in Antarctica for extended periods; whale sightings; and looking at the variety of seals and bird life.

A tour by ship of the Antarctic Peninsula has another attraction. Deception Island, located off the northern tip of the peninsula, was formed by a volcano. Its collapsed volcanic cone, called a 'caldera', provides one of the world's safest natural harbours. The volcano is still active, with the most recent eruptions occurring in 1991–1992. The volcanic activity forces hot water up through narrow fissures along the shore at a place called Pendulum Cove. The water is not deep enough for swimming but bathing in the thermally heated waters surrounded by ice makes it a popular tourist attraction.

Most cruises to the Antarctic Peninsula leave from the relatively nearby port of Ushuaia in Argentina, between the warmer months of November and March when the winter pack ice breaks up.

A visit to this unique and fascinating place is an experience unlike anywhere else on the planet.

Juan Rodriguez, Argentina

Use the report on page 47 to complete the page.

1. Title

(a) Title (headline)

_____

(b) Is it an appropriate headline?   **yes** ☐ **no** ☐

Why/Why not? _____

_____

_____

2. Classification

Write four adjectives from the classification section that describe Antarctica.

3. Description

(a) What is the main idea of paragraph 3 of the description section?

(b) Look in paragraph 4 to find the correct terms for:

(i) a collapsed volcanic cone

_____

(ii) a narrow opening in the Earth's surface.

_____

(c) List five present tense verbs from paragraph 3.

_____ _____ _____ _____ _____

(d) Change these sentences about Antarctica to the third person.

(i) I am roughly circular in shape, and my peninsula is my most populated region.

_____

_____

(ii) I am one of the best places you can visit.

_____

(iii) You should visit me. _____

4. Conclusion

(a) What comment does the reporter, Juan Rodriguez, make about Antarctica?

_____

_____

(b) Write your own conclusion.

1. Plan a report for the travel section of a newspaper or magazine about a place you have visited, have learnt about, or research one you would like to visit. Remember to include accurate information, use the present tense and write in the third person.

Title

A catchy headline.

Classification

A subhead or general statement about the subject of the report.

Description

Divide the description into sections.

Conclusion

It may contain an expert or personal opinion or be a summarising comment.

2. Write your report.

3. Edit your work.

Structural and language features are shown on the left and right of the text below.

Title	**The human voice**	
Definition – one or more sentences that state what the explanation is about	Your voice is your very own personal musical instrument. It can be defined as the sounds you produce through your mouth.	• subject-specific vocabulary; e.g. **lungs**, **vocal cords**
Description – provides accurate description and facts	Human voices produce sound using three main parts — the **lungs**, the **vocal cords** and the pharynx (throat). Other parts of the body used include the tongue, the jaw, the teeth, the lips, facial muscles and the hard and soft palates on the roof of the mouth.	• majority of verbs in simple present tense; e.g. **produce**, **vibrate**
	Lungs	
	The voice is powered by air. When you breathe, a column of air passes up from your lungs, through the trachea (windpipe) and is forced over and through your vocal cords.	
	The lungs control the loudness or softness of sound. When more air is forced through the vocal cords, the louder the sounds produced will be, for example yelling or screaming. When less air is forced through the lungs, softer sounds are produced, such as whispering.	• linking words to show cause and effect; e.g. **Finally**, **before**
	Vocal cords	
	The two vocal cords are folds of tissue that stretch across a cavity called the voice box (larynx) in your throat. The air makes the vocal cords vibrate, like windchimes, creating sound. You can see how this works by holding two of your fingers together in front of your mouth. Blow air through your fingers as you move them around. You should be able to hear faint sounds. If you place your hand halfway down the front of your neck and speak, you will also be able to feel your vocal cords vibrating.	• information is organised into paragraphs
	The thickness and length of individual vocal cords **produce** different pitches when they **vibrate**—just like the strings on a guitar. Men usually have lower voices than women because their vocal cords are generally longer and thicker.	
	The pharynx	
	The pharynx (throat) is connected to the larynx and divides into two sections—one going to the mouth and the other to the nose. The sound from the vibrating vocal cords passes up through the throat **before** going through the mouth and nasal cavity and being produced as sound.	
	Other parts of the body	
	Finally, the sound is 'chopped up' into different sounds by the tongue, jaw, teeth, lips, facial muscles and the hard and soft palates on the roof of the mouth. The type of sounds produced will depend on the mouth and nasal cavity. This is why some people can sing well and others can't!	
Conclusion – an evaluation or interesting comment	Humans can use their voices to produce an amazing variety of sounds, from whispers to shouts and from humming to opera singing! How many ways do you use your voice every day?	

Teacher information

• Explanations usually outline how something occurs, works or is made. This particular explanation shows how something works.

• Allow the pupils to read the text independently. Once the text is read ask selected pupils to explain how the human voice works to ensure that they have understood the explanation clearly.

• Identify and discuss the structural features indicated above and ask pupils to identify specific examples of the language features. Discuss how important diagrams are as an aid to accompany explanations.

• Pupils should then complete the analysis on page 52.

• Model the planning and writing of an explanation using the framework on page 53. Pupils may wish to suggest a suitable topic; e.g. how the heart works. The pupils can then follow this example to plan and write their explanations about the function of the ear.

• Pupils may need to use encyclopedias or other resources to research information for their explanations.

• Pupils could write their explanations and add three-dimensional models for display. (Display)

• The pupils' explanations could be given as an oral presentation to other members of the class when learning about systems and functions of the human body. (Purpose/Audience/Context)

Answers

Page 52

1–2. Teacher check

3. (a) air from lungs → trachea → vocal cords → larynx → pharynx → mouth and nasal cavity

    (b) Some examples may include:

      (i) and, such as, finally, before etc.

      (ii) produce, include, control, makes etc.

      (iii) pharynx, lungs, vocal cords etc.

    (c) Teacher check

4. Teacher check

The human voice

Your voice is your very own personal musical instrument. It can be defined as 'the sounds you produce through your mouth'.

Human voices produce sound using three main parts—the lungs, the vocal cords and the pharynx (throat). Other parts of the body used include the tongue, the jaw, the teeth, the lips, facial muscles and the hard and soft palates on the roof of the mouth.

Lungs

The voice is powered by air. When you breathe, a column of air passes up from your lungs, through the trachea (windpipe) and is forced over and through your vocal cords.

The lungs control the loudness or softness of sound. When more air is forced through the vocal cords, the louder the sounds produced will be, for example when yelling or screaming. When less air is forced through the lungs, softer sounds are produced, such as whispering.

Vocal cords

The two vocal cords are folds of tissue that stretch across a cavity called the voice box (larynx) in your throat. The air makes the vocal cords vibrate, like windchimes, creating sound. You can see how this works by holding two of your fingers together in front of your mouth. Blow air through your fingers as you move them around. You should be able to hear faint sounds. If you place your hand halfway down the front of your neck and speak, you will also be able to feel your vocal cords vibrating.

The thickness and length of individual vocal cords produce different pitches when they vibrate—just like the strings on a guitar. Men usually have lower voices than women because their vocal cords are generally longer and thicker.

The pharynx

The pharynx (throat) is connected to the larynx and divides into two sections—one going to the mouth and the other to the nose. The sound from the vibrating vocal cords passes up through the throat before going through the mouth and nasal cavity and being produced as sound.

Other parts of the body

Finally, the sound is 'chopped up' into different sounds by the tongue, jaw, teeth, lips, facial muscles and the hard and soft palates on the roof of the mouth. The type of sounds produced will depend on the mouth and nasal cavity. This is why some people can sing well and others can't!

Humans can use their voices to produce an amazing variety of sounds, from whispers to shouts and from humming to opera singing! How many ways do you use your voice every day?

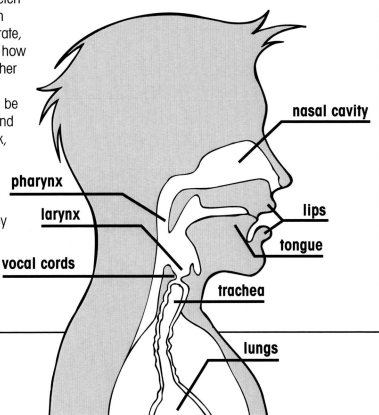

nasal cavity

pharynx

larynx

vocal cords

lips

tongue

trachea

lungs

Examining explanation

Use the explanation on page 51 to complete the page.

1. Title

Write an alternative,
appropriate title.

2. Definition

(a) Tick the boxes.

    (i) A precise statement is given. ☐

    (ii) A definition is provided. ☐

(b) Write two keywords from the definition.

3. Description

(a) Draw a very simple flow chart to illustrate the main body parts involved in producing sound.

(b) Write three examples from the explanation of each of the following:

    (i) linking words

    (ii) present tense verbs

    (iii)vocabulary relating to the topic

(c) Tick the boxes to indicate your opinion.

    (i) The information is clear. ☐

    (ii) The information is in a logical order. ☐

    (iii)The information is correct. ☐

4. Conclusion

Write a new conclusion for this text that contains a different interesting comment.

1. Plan an explanation about how the ear works. Include a diagram.

Title

Definition

Description

Conclusion

2. Write your explanation.

3. Edit your work.

Structural and language features are shown on the left and right of the text below.

Title	**Compact discs**
Definition – one or more sentences that state what the explanation is about	Compact discs are optical discs on which digital information is stored. They may be used to hold your favourite music, **data**, computer software or images. But have you ever wondered what they actually are or how they work?
Description – information presented in logical order	Compact discs or CDs can be found everywhere. Millions are created and distributed each year in one form or another because they are easy and cheap to make. Experiments on CDs began in the 1970s and by the early 1990s compact discs were on the market. Now, they are the most common format in which to buy or store **audio** recording. CDs may consist of up to 99 stereo tracks and can hold between 74 and 90 minutes of audio.
	Compact discs consist of a number of different layers.
	The first layer is made from soft plastic. This makes up the thickest part of the CD but it is actually very thin (usually about 1.2 mm thick). It helps to protect the data that will be put onto the CD. When the finished CD is later put into a CD player, the soft plastic layer will also act as a lens to help the laser in the CD player focus on the data—just like a lens in a pair of glasses!
	The second layer is the most important one — the data layer. The data **is transferred** onto the CD by a laser. The laser does this by creating millions of tiny ridges and flat areas in a single, continuous track on the CD, spiralling from the inside to the outside. The width of one of the ridges is less than that of a strand of your hair!
	The third layer is a shiny, aluminium coating which is placed onto the data layer. To read the ridges and flat areas, a CD player **passes** a laser beam over them. As the CD rotates, this beam is reflected by the aluminium coating to a sensor inside the player which interprets the ridges and flat areas as different types of sounds. This shiny coating is what you can see when you look at the playing side of a CD.
	Finally, a thin, hard, plastic coating is added to the CD to protect the data and reflective layers from dirt and dust. It also forms a surface for a label, telling you exactly what you are listening to! The label contains the title, graphics, artist and any other information to help identify exactly what is on the CD.
	The small hole in the middle of the disc is used by a clamp or clip device within the CD player to hold it in place and allow it to be rotated. When CDs were first invented, the hole was exactly the same size as an earlier Dutch 10-cent piece.
	When a CD is placed into a CD player, three main things will happen — a motor spins the disc in a precise number of revolutions each minute; a laser and lens system locates and reads the ridges and a tracking mechanism moves the laser so that the beam can follow the spiral track.
Conclusion – an evaluation or interesting comment	CDs are a clever invention. They are capable of excellent sound quality and easy to use. Can they be improved upon? It is difficult to imagine—but is certainly likely to happen one day!

Language features (right margin):
- subject-specific vocabulary; e.g. **data**, **audio**
- majority of verbs in simple present tense; e.g. **is transferred, passes**
- linking words to show cause and effect; e.g. **Finally, When**
- information is organised into paragraphs

Teacher information

- Explanations usually outline how something occurs, works or is made. This particular explanation shows how something works.

- Allow the pupils to read the text independently. Once the text is read, ask selected pupils to explain how a CD works to ensure that they have understood the explanation clearly.

- Identify and discuss the structural features indicated above and ask pupils to identify specific examples of the language features. Discuss the importance of diagrams as an aid to explanations.

- Pupils should then complete the analysis on page 56.

- Model the planning and writing of an explanation using the framework on page 57. Pupils may wish to suggest a suitable topic; e.g. how the democratic system operates. The pupils can then follow this example to plan and write their explanations about how television works.

- Pupils will need to use library or Internet resources to research how television works before commencing their explanation plan on page 57. Pupils may research in groups or pairs to obtain their information.

- Pupils could write their explanations and display each behind a television screen shape with illustrations of their favourite television characters around it. (Display)

- The pupils' explanations could be given as an oral presentation to the members of another class. (Purpose/ Audience)

- The new explanations could be written in conjunction with a unit about technology, different types of communication or the media. (Context)

Answers

Page 56

1. Compact discs
2. Teacher check
3. (a) – (b) Teacher check
   (c) Answers will vary but may include
      (i) laser, data, track etc.
      (ii) forms, contains, hold etc.
      (iii) and, but, When etc.
   (d) Answers will vary but may include 'The width of one of the ridges is less than that of a strand of your hair! etc.
4. Teacher check

Compact discs

Compact discs are optical discs on which digital information is stored. They may be used to hold your favourite music, data, computer software or images. But have you ever wondered what they actually are or how they work?

Compact discs or CDs can be found everywhere. Millions are created and distributed each year in one form or another because they are easy and cheap to make. Experiments on CDs began in the 1970s and by the early 1990s compact discs were on the market. Now, they are the most common format in which to buy or store audio recording. CDs may consist of up to 99 stereo tracks and can hold between 74 and 90 minutes of audio.

Compact discs consist of a number of different layers.

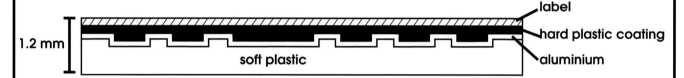

1.2 mm — soft plastic — label — hard plastic coating — aluminium

The first layer is made from soft plastic. This makes up the thickest part of the CD but it is actually very thin (usually about 1.2 mm thick). It helps to protect the data that will be put onto the CD. When the finished CD is later put into a CD player, the soft plastic layer will also act as a lens to help the laser in the CD player focus on the data—just like a lens in a pair of glasses!

The second layer is the most important one — the data layer. The data is transferred onto the CD by a laser. The laser does this by creating millions of tiny ridges and flat areas in a single, continuous track on the CD, spiralling from the inside to the outside. The width of one of the ridges is less than that of a strand of your hair!

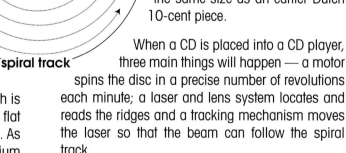

spiral track

The third layer is a shiny, aluminium coating which is placed onto the data layer. To read the ridges and flat areas, a CD player passes a laser beam over them. As the CD rotates, this beam is reflected by the aluminium coating to a sensor inside the player which interprets the ridges and flat areas as different types of sounds. This shiny coating is what you can see when you look at the playing side of a CD.

Finally, a thin, hard, plastic coating is added to the CD to protect the data and reflective layers from dirt and dust. It also forms a surface for a label, telling you exactly what you are listening to! The label contains the title, graphics, artist and any other information to help identify exactly what is on the CD.

The small hole in the middle of the disc is used by a clamp or clip device within the CD player to hold it in place and allow it to be rotated. When CDs were first invented, the hole was exactly the same size as an earlier Dutch 10-cent piece.

When a CD is placed into a CD player, three main things will happen — a motor spins the disc in a precise number of revolutions each minute; a laser and lens system locates and reads the ridges and a tracking mechanism moves the laser so that the beam can follow the spiral track.

CDs are a clever invention. They are capable of excellent sound quality and easy to use. Can they be improved upon? It is difficult to imagine—but is certainly likely to happen one day!

Use the explanation on page 55 to complete the page.

1. Title

The title is

2. Definition

What is a compact disc?

3. Description

(a) Tick the boxes.

(i) The information in the description is relevant and seems correct. ☐

(ii) The information is given in a logical order. ☐

(iii) The information is clear and stated simply. ☐

(b) Explain your reason for any box(es) which were not ticked.

_____

_____

_____

_____

(c) Write two examples of each of the language features.

(i) technical or terms specific to the topic

_____

(ii) verbs in the present tense

_____

(iii) linking words to show cause and effect

_____

(d) Some interesting snippets of information are given to maintain reader interest. Choose and copy one of these below.

4. Conclusion

Write a new conclusion for this text. Include a different, interesting comment.

_____

_____

_____

_____

1. Plan an explanation about how a television works.

Title

Definition

Description

Conclusion

2. Write your explanation.

3. Edit your work.

Structural and language features are shown on the left and right of the text below.

Title	**Peckish plants**	
Definition – one or more sentences that state what the explanation is about	Meat-eating or 'carnivorous' plants are plants which attract, kill and digest animal life forms in order to absorb the nutrients needed to survive.	• subject-specific vocabulary; e.g. **nutrients**, **prey**
Description – information presented in logical order	Most plants get the water and **nutrients** they need from the soil. Carnivorous plants grow in wet swamps or marshes where the soil is very poor, so they must get nitrogen and other minerals from the bodies of the animals that they catch and eat. Carnivorous plants cannot reach their **prey** so they use different methods to lure and catch them.

Some carnivorous plants give off a sweet smell like nectar which attracts flies, bees or ants. The pitcher plant uses this method. The insects are attracted by the sweet smell, then they are trapped by thick bristles on the leaves. **Eventually**, they slide down into a jug-like container that has been formed by the plant's leaves. This container is filled with rainwater, in which the insects drown. The plant **then** creates juices which digest or break down the insect—giving the plant a meal! One type of large pitcher plant, the nepenthe, has a varied diet. As well as insects, it can trap and digest frogs and even small mammals like rats! A nepenthe may hold about four litres of water.

Another type of carnivorous plant is the sundew. Its leaves grow in the shape of a rosette and are covered in hairs. The hairs have beads of sticky fluid on them. Like the pitcher plant, insects are attracted to the sundew's nectar. When the insect lands on the sundew, it soon finds itself stuck on some of the hairs. Once it is caught, other hairs wrap around the insect. The insect soon becomes covered in sticky fluid which causes it to suffocate. The sundew then produces digestive juices which dissolve the soft parts of the insect's body.

Probably the most well-known carnivorous plant is the Venus flytrap. The upper part of this plant's leaves, the 'lobes', look a bit like open clamshells. Sensitive hairs grow on the inside of the lobes. When an insect lands on a lobe and touches the hairs, it triggers the 'clamshell' to spring shut, capturing the insect inside. The trap is made even more secure by the teeth-like bristles that grow on the edge of the lobes and interlock when the lobes spring shut. The lobes then produce digestive juices to dissolve the soft parts of the insect. Once the plant has absorbed the food, the lobes open up again, ready for another victim!

Other plants give off a smell like decay which **attracts** flies and other insects. Many carnivorous plants have bright colours or patterns to attract animal life. Others have leaves covered with sparkling droplets which are bright and have a sweet smell. There are also plants which give off a chemical which paralyses the insect. It then **releases** an enzyme which breaks down the body of the insect so that the plant can eat it. | • linking words to show cause and effect; e.g. **Eventually**, **then**

• majority of verbs in simple present tense; e.g. **attracts**, **releases**

• information is organised into paragraphs |
| **Conclusion –** an evaluation or interesting comment | Carnivorous plants are often thought to exist only in the imagination of science fiction writers. But now you know they are real. And by the way, there are no carnivorous plants large enough to eat humans – at least, no-one has discovered one yet …! | |

Teacher information

- Explanations usually outline how something occurs, works or is made. This particular explanation shows how something works.
- Allow the pupils to read the text independently. Discuss the text to ensure that pupils have understood the explanation clearly.
- Identify and discuss the structural features indicated above and ask pupils to identify specific examples of the language features.
- Pupils should then complete the analysis on page 60.
- Model the planning and writing of an explanation using the framework on page 61. Pupils may wish to suggest a suitable topic such as how an animal digests its food. The pupils can then follow this example to plan and write their own explanations about how a particular plant or animal gets its water and nutrients.
- Pupils may wish to use library or Internet resources to research before commencing their explanation plan on page 61.

- Pupils could write their explanations and display them mounted on a plant or animal background. (Display)
- The pupils' explanations could be shared and discussed with other class members. (Purpose/Audience)
- The new explanations could be written in conjunction with a science unit. (Context)

Answers
Page 60
1–2. Teacher check
3. (a) Teacher check
   (b) Answers will vary but may include:
      (i) nectar, bristles, hairs, insects, juices, digest etc.
      (ii) get, need, grow, slide, wrap, lands, triggers etc.
      (iii) so, then, also, eventually, and etc.
3. (c) Teacher check
4. Teacher check

Peckish plants

Meat-eating or 'carnivorous' plants are plants which attract, kill and digest animal life forms in order to absorb the nutrients needed to survive.

Most plants get the water and nutrients they need from the soil. Carnivorous plants grow in wet swamps or marshes where the soil is very poor, so they must get nitrogen and other minerals from the bodies of the animals that they catch and eat. Carnivorous plants cannot reach their prey so they use different methods to lure and catch them.

Some carnivorous plants give off a sweet smell like nectar which attracts flies, bees or ants. The pitcher plant uses this method. The insects are attracted by the sweet smell, then they are trapped by thick bristles on the leaves. Eventually, they slide down into a jug-like container that has been formed by the plant's leaves. This container is filled with rainwater, in which the insects drown. The plant then creates juices which digest or break down the insect—giving the plant a meal! One type of large pitcher plant, the nepenthe, has a varied diet. As well as insects, it can trap and digest frogs and even small mammals like rats! A nepenthe may hold about four litres of water.

Another type of carnivorous plant is the sundew. Its leaves grow in the shape of a rosette and are covered in hairs. The hairs have beads of sticky fluid on them. Like the pitcher plant, insects are attracted to the sundew's nectar. When the insect lands on the sundew, it soon finds itself stuck on some of the hairs. Once it is caught, other hairs wrap around the insect. The insect soon becomes covered in sticky fluid which causes it to suffocate. The sundew then produces digestive juices which dissolve the soft parts of the insect's body.

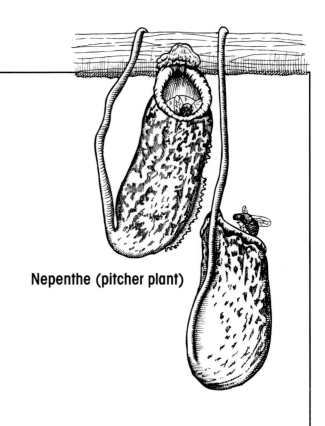

Nepenthe (pitcher plant)

Probably the most well-known carnivorous plant is the Venus flytrap. The upper part of this plant's leaves, the 'lobes', look a bit like open clamshells. Sensitive hairs grow on the inside of the lobes. When an insect lands on a lobe and touches the hairs, it triggers the 'clamshell' to spring shut, capturing the insect inside. The trap is made even more secure by the teeth-like bristles that grow on the edge of the lobes and interlock when the lobes spring shut. The lobes then produce digestive juices to dissolve the soft parts of the insect. Once the plant has absorbed the food, the lobes open up again, ready for another victim!

Other plants give off a smell like decay which attracts flies and other insects. Many carnivorous plants have bright colours or patterns to attract animal life. Others have leaves covered with sparkling droplets which are bright and have a sweet smell. There are also plants which give off a chemical which paralyses the insect. It then releases an enzyme which breaks down the body of the insect so that the plant can eat it.

Carnivorous plants are often thought to exist only in the imagination of science fiction writers. But now you know they are real. And by the way, there are no carnivorous plants large enough to eat humans – at least, no-one has discovered one yet ... !

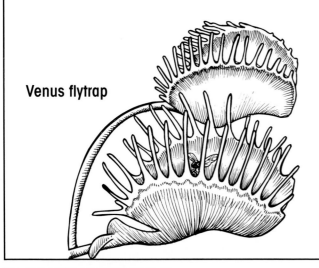

Venus flytrap

Examining explanation ③

Use the explanation on page 59 to complete the page.

1. Title

Why did the writer choose this title?

2. Definition

Is the definition provided precise or is more information needed? **yes** ☐ **no** ☐

Give reasons for your answer.

3. Description

(a) Use bullet points to summarise the important information in the description. Write them in the order in which they were presented.

(b) Write two examples of each of the language features.

   (i) technical or terms specific to the topic

_____

   (ii) verbs in the present tense

_____

   (iii) linking words to show cause and effect

_____

(c) Select the most interesting piece of information and write it below in your own words.

_____

_____

_____

_____

_____

_____

4. Conclusion

(a) Did the conclusion give: an evaluation? **yes** ☐ **no** ☐   a comment? **yes** ☐ **no** ☐

(b) Write a new conclusion. _____

_____

_____

1. Plan an explanation about how a plant or animal gets its water and nutrients. Include a diagram.

Title

Definition

Description

Conclusion

2. Write your explanation.

3. Edit your work.

Structural and language features are shown on the left and right of the text below.

Title	**Class captain**	
Introduction – one or more sentences that state the issue	'Class members of 6A, I think that I would make an **excellent** candidate for class captain and that you **should** vote for me for a number of reasons.	• a variety of controlling and emotive words; e.g. **should**, **excellent**
Arguments – presented in logical manner with supporting details, usually from strongest to weakest	The first reason for voting for me is that I am an active member of the school community. I am a member of the school choir which has represented the school when singing at the Senior Citizens' Club during Seniors' Week and at the combined Schools' Christmas concert and community events such as Carols in the Park. I have been a pupil 'librarian' for two years and sports monitor this year. The second reason is that I have been a member of this school all of my school life. I started school when Mr Brown was the head teacher and Mrs George was the infant teacher. I saw the new playground equipment being put in and the sun shelter installed to cover the sandpit and climbing equipment area. I watched the rose gardens being built **when** Mrs Stokes retired and the new computer lending system installed in the library. I know all the teaching and ancillary staff at the school and I am very familiar with the school environment. Another reason is that I am very interested in community activities as well. I worked with other community groups to pick up rubbish from around the lake near my house on Clean Up Day. I also planted trees along the reclaimed open space near the river for Tree Day with my family. The final reason is that I am a 'well-rounded' person. I enjoy playing sport at school and on the weekends I play cricket in summer and football in winter. I enjoy listening to music, watching television and DVDs and reading comic books. My favourite computer game is 'Robotic Wars'. There are five people in my family and I am the oldest child with two younger sisters.	• paragraphs used to state and elaborate on each point • a variety of conjunctions; e.g. **because**, **when** • persuasive language is used so others will agree with the writer's point of view; e.g. **very involved**, **responsible**
Conclusion – restates the writer's position and summarises arguments	So, to conclude, you should vote for me for class captain **because** I am **very involved** in school activities, I know the school and staff well, I am involved in community activities and I am a **responsible**, well-rounded person. Please vote for me!'	

Teacher information

- This discussion is in the form of a speech to persuade class members to vote for the writer.
- Allow the pupils to read the discussion.
- Discuss the title and its suitability, the introduction, the arguments, the conclusion and the language features on the right of the text.
- Pupils complete the analysis on page 64.
- Before pupils attempt to use the discussion plan on page 65 to plan their own discussion, model the process of planning then writing a discussion about being voted 'Teacher of the Year'. Emphasis should be placed on listing a number of arguments with supporting details and determining which argument is the strongest and will go first.
- Pupils need to understand that the plan is for ideas and that they will write their real discussion later.
- Pupils write a discussion to participate in a real class captain voting process. (Context/Purpose/Audience)
- Pupils may publish their discussion using computers and print them to allow class members to reread them when making their decision about who to vote for. (Publishing/Audience)

Answers

Page 64
1. Teacher check
2. (a) The issue is the election of the class captain.
   (b) He wants the pupils to vote for him.
3. (a) active school community member, long-time school member, active in the community, 'well-rounded' person
   (b) Teacher check
   (c) Teacher check
4. Teacher check

Class captain

'Class members of 6A,

I think that I would make an excellent candidate for class captain and that you should vote for me for a number of reasons.

The first reason for voting for me is that I am an active member of the school community. I am a member of the school choir which has represented the school when singing at the Senior Citizens' Club during Seniors' Week and at the combined Schools' Christmas concert and community events such as Carols in the Park. I have been a pupil 'librarian' for two years and sports monitor this year.

The second reason is that I have been a member of this school all of my school life. I started school when Mr Brown was the head teacher and Mrs George was the infant teacher. I saw the new playground equipment being put in and the sun shelter installed to cover the sandpit and climbing equipment area. I watched the rose gardens being built when Mrs Stokes retired and the new computer lending system installed in the library. I know all the teaching and ancillary staff at the school and I am very familiar with the school environment.

Another reason is that I am very interested in community activities as well. I worked with other community groups to pick up rubbish from around the lake near my house on Clean Up Day. I also planted trees along the reclaimed open space near the river for Tree Day with my family.

The final reason is that I am a 'well-rounded' person. I enjoy playing sport at school and on the weekends I play cricket in summer and football in winter. I enjoy listening to music, watching television and DVDs and reading comic books. My favourite computer game is 'Robotic Wars'. There are five people in my family and I am the oldest child with two younger sisters.

So, to conclude, you should vote for me for class captain because I am very involved in school activities, I know the school and staff well, I am involved in community activities and I am a responsible, well-rounded person.

Please vote for me!'

Use the discussion on page 63 to complete the page.

1. Title

(a) Is the title of the discussion appropriate?

yes ☐   no ☐

(b) Write an alternative title which would still suit this discussion.

2. Introduction

(a) What issue is the speaker addressing?

_____

_____

(b) What does he want the pupils to do?

_____

_____

_____

3. Arguments

(a) Write bullet points to show the main arguments presented.

- _____

  _____

- _____

  _____

- _____

  _____

- _____

  _____

(b) Did the speaker:

(i) present his arguments in logical order?   yes ☐ no ☐

(ii) start with the strongest argument?   yes ☐ no ☐

(iii) use supporting details to support each argument?   yes ☐ no ☐

CLASS CAPTAIN

(c) Would you vote for this speaker? yes ☐ no ☐

Why/Why not? _____

_____

_____

4. Conclusion

The conclusion should restate the writer's position.

(a) Did the writer achieve this aim? yes ☐ no ☐

Explain how. _____

_____

1. Plan a discussion to encourage other class members to vote for you to be class captain. Give your discussion a different title from the one on page 63.

Title

Introduction

Arguments

Conclusion

2. Write your discussion.

3. Edit your work.

Structural and language features are shown on the left and right of the text below.

Title	**Riverside Park**
Introduction – one or more sentences that state the issue	Dear Editor, I am writing to complain about the state of our local park, which **has to be** fixed up.
Arguments – presented in logical manner with supporting details, usually from strongest to weakest	Riverside Park backs onto the playing fields of our school. **When** we are on the field playing at break times, often one of our balls rolls into the park. Sometimes it is nearly impossible to find our ball among the long grass so that we can continue our game! Who knows what else may be lurking among the long grass and weeds! There used to be a nice garden with a lot of rocks around it along one side. It's just as well that we don't have to go over there to get our ball **because** we might trip over hidden rocks and break our leg! There's also an old car tyre and a beaten-up bike lying around. We are **taking our life in our hands** every time we venture in there to get our ball! It's not a safe place! I've seen ripped plastic garbage bags with rubbish spread around everywhere! Once or twice I've even seen used needles lying near a clump of trees! It was lucky none of us pricked our fingers on any of those or we might have got sick! It's just not healthy to have an area like that so close to a school! When we drive past Riverside Park to go to football, I often think how ugly it looks! It's really a shame because **if** all the rubbish was cleared away and the grass mowed and the gardens tidied, it would be a nice place to play. There could even be some tables and chairs to have a picnic and some climbing equipment for the little kids! If it looked nice people would use it more often! At the moment it just makes the whole neighbourhood look untidy! I think the council should do something to fix it up! We had a 'Clean Up Day' at our school last year and lots of parents came to clean up the school grounds and to put in some playground equipment for the little kids. I bet they would be happy to do the same thing to Riverside Park! Our school playground is really small and the little kids keep getting in the way when we try to play football and other games! If Riverside Park was cleaned up really well, the school might be able to get permission to let the kids use some of it for playing on during break times! Then we would have more room for everyone to play!
Conclusion – restates the writer's position and summarises arguments	At the moment Riverside Park is **unsafe**, unhealthy, ugly and a **useless space**! Riverside Park could be a nice place instead of an eyesore. It must be fixed up!

- a variety of controlling and emotive words; e.g. **has to be**, **taking our life in our hands**

- paragraphs used to state and elaborate on each point

- a variety of conjunctions; e.g. **When**, **because**, **if**

- persuasive language is used so others will agree with the writer's point of view; e.g. **unsafe**, **useless space**

Teacher information

- This discussion is in the form of a letter to the editor to persuade people to do something about the state of a community facility.
- Allow the pupils to read the discussion.
- Discuss the title, the introduction, the arguments, the conclusion and the language features.
- Pupils complete the analysis on page 68.
- Before pupils attempt to use the discussion plan on page 69 to plan their own discussion, model the process of planning then writing a discussion about a relevant community problem. Emphasis should be placed on listing a number of arguments with supporting details and determining which argument is the strongest and will go first.
- Pupils need to understand that the plan is for ideas and that they will write their real discussion later.
- Pupils complete a discussion to show positive action towards a community problem causing concern. (Context/Purpose)
- Pupils could use their discussion as the basis for an oral presentation to the class. (Purpose/Audience)
- Pupil could publish their discussion on a computer and display it on a decorated letter shape. (Publishing/Display)

Answers

Page 68

1–2. Teacher check

3. (a)

Park is unsafe.	Park is unhealthy.	Park looks awful!	Park would give more room to play
• long grass and weeds which may hide nasty things • hidden hazards such as rocks • dangerous objects such as old tyres and bikes	• old needles lying around	• rubbish lying around • untidy grass • messy gardens • no tables and chairs • no play equipment	• close to school • school playing area small • some kids could play on it to leave more room for others to play in different areas

(b) Teacher check

4. Teacher check

Riverside Park

Dear Editor,

I am writing to complain about the state of our local park, which has to be fixed up.

Riverside Park backs onto the playing fields of our school. When we are on the field playing at break times, often one of our balls rolls into the park. Sometimes it is nearly impossible to find our ball among the long grass so that we can continue our game! Who knows what else may be lurking among the long grass and weeds! There used to be a nice garden with a lot of rocks around it along one side. It's just as well that we don't have to go over there to get our ball because we might trip over hidden rocks and break our leg! There's also an old car tyre and a beaten-up bike lying around. We are taking our life in our hands every time we venture in there to get our ball! It's not a safe place!

I've seen ripped plastic garbage bags with rubbish spread around everywhere! Once or twice I've even seen used needles lying near a clump of trees! It was lucky none of us pricked our fingers on any of those or we might have got sick! It's just not healthy to have an area like that so close to a school!

When we drive past Riverside Park to go to football, I often think how ugly it looks! It's really a shame because if all the rubbish was cleared away and the grass mowed and the gardens tidied, it would be a nice place to play. There could even be some tables and chairs to have a picnic and some climbing equipment for the little kids! If it looked nice people would use it more often! At the moment it just makes the whole neighbourhood look untidy! I think the council should do something to fix it up! We had a 'Clean Up Day' at our school last year and lots of parents came to clean up the school grounds and to put in some playground equipment for the little kids. I bet they would be happy to do the same thing to Riverside Park!

Our school playground is really small and the little kids keep getting in the way when we try to play football and other games! If Riverside Park was cleaned up really well, the school might be able to get permission to let the kids use some of it for playing on during break times! Then we would have more room for everyone to play!

At the moment Riverside Park is unsafe, unhealthy, ugly and a useless space! Riverside Park could be a nice place instead of an eyesore. It must be fixed up!

Use the discussion on page 67 to complete the page.

1. Title

Write two stronger, more persuasive titles for the discussion.

(a)

(b)

2. Introduction

In your own words, write a different introduction. Be sure to state what needs to happen and your position.

_____

_____

_____

_____

_____

_____

_____

3. Arguments

(a) The writer gave four arguments for fixing up Riverside Park. Use the boxes to briefly state what they were and underneath write the details which were given to support each argument.

☐	☐	☐	☐

(b) In each box, number the arguments in the order you would have written them.

4. Conclusion

Write a new conclusion for the discussion which summarises the arguments and restates the writer's opinion.

_____

_____

_____

_____

1. Plan a discussion in the form of a letter to an editor of a newspaper about a community problem. State your position and what you believe should happen.

Title

Introduction

Arguments

Conclusion

2. Write your discussion.

3. Edit your work.

Structural and language features are shown on the left and right of the text below.

Title	Jumping Jiminy! What a journal!
Introduction – one or more sentences that state the issue and the writer's position	Pupils, do you muddle through the week, flitting from one social event to another, going here and there, until Friday is suddenly upon you? You arrive at school and the teacher says 'Hand your homework in now, please! With great dismay you realise that you have forgotten to do your homework for the week! Another lunchtime spent doing homework instead of being outside with your friends! Jumping Jiminy **has the answer** for you! Jumping Jiminy has just released a homework journal **to beat all** homework journals! It is guaranteed to solve your homework woes!
Arguments – presented in logical manner with supporting details, usually from strongest to weakest	Made of durable, washable, high-tech material, the Jumping Jiminy Journal is bright and attractive so that it cannot be easily forgotten. It even glows in the dark! The sturdy, high-tech material from which it is made is impervious to mashed potato, greasy chips, squashed peas and gravy. It even withstands pizza sauce and Coke™. So no more excuses about having to eat dinner instead of doing homework! Do both at the same time **and** have more time to watch television, play computer games or socialise with your friends! The Jumping Jiminy Journal is able to withstand the strain! The handy organiser has a built-in memory chip. Once programmed, a flashing alarm and thoroughly annoying voice lets you know very loudly that you need to do some homework! Best of all there is a high-frequency portable attachment **which** may be carried with you. This will interrupt you no matter what you are doing and where you are to remind you about doing your homework! What a great bonus! The Jumping Jiminy Journal comes with its own calculator and a supply of biros, pencils, erasers and blank paper. There is a convenient compartment for a mobile phone and a portable music player. It also has a handy shoulder pouch to allow you to carry it wherever you go!
Conclusion – restates the writer's position and summarises arguments	This is by far the **greatest** invention since the school bell! Every pupil **should** have one and all parents **will want** to buy one for their child! The Jumping Jiminy Journal is easy to see, easy to hear, reliable, durable and convenient! The Jumping Jiminy Journal! You need one! Get it now!

- persuasive language is used so others will agree with the writers point of view; e.g. **has the answer**, **to beat all**

- paragraphs used to state and elaborate on each point

- a variety of conjunctions; e.g. **and**, **which**

- a variety of controlling and emotive words; e.g. **greatest**, **should**, **will want**

Teacher information

- This discussion is in the form of an advertisement to encourage school pupils and their parents to purchase a Jumping Jiminy Journal.
- Allow the pupils to read the discussion. Selected pupils may be chosen to read the discussion in an expressive manner to illustrate the emotive language used.
- Discuss the title suitability, the introduction, the arguments, the conclusion and the language features.
- Discuss the reality of such a journal existing and its usefulness.
- Pupils complete the analysis on page 72.
- Before pupils attempt to use the discussion plan on page 73 to plan their own discussion, model the process of planning then writing a discussion in the form of an advertisement for a new computer game. Emphasis should be placed on the persuasive language with supporting details used to convince readers to buy the product.
- Pupils need to understand that the plan is for ideas and that they will write their real discussion later.
- Pupils complete a discussion when completing a technology or science unit. (Context)
- Pupils could use their discussion to give a dramatic presentation to their own class, parents or to entertain a younger class. (Purpose/Audience)
- Pupils could publish their discussion on computer and display it on a large sheet of art paper with an imaginative sketch of their portable music player. (Publishing/Display)

Answers

Page 72
1. Teacher check
2. (a) 2
   (b) Teacher check
   (c) Pupils should have ticked both boxes.
3. (a) made of durable, high-tech material; programmed to remind you to do homework; includes other accessories
   (b) Teacher check
   (c) Answers will vary.
   (d) Teacher check
4. Yes; Teacher check

Jumping Jiminy!
What a journal!
YOU NEED ONE!

GET IT NOW!

Pupils, do you muddle through the week, flitting from one social event to another, going here and there, until Friday is suddenly upon you? You arrive at school and the teacher says 'Hand your homework in now, please!' With great dismay you realise that you have forgotten to do your homework for the week! Another lunchtime spent doing homework instead of being outside with your friends!

Jumping Jiminy has the answer for you! Jumping Jiminy has just released a homework journal to beat all homework journals! It is guaranteed to solve your homework woes!

Made of durable, washable, high-tech material, the Jumping Jiminy Journal is bright and attractive so that it cannot be easily forgotten. It even glows in the dark!

The sturdy, high-tech material from which it is made is impervious to mashed potato, greasy chips, squashed peas and gravy. It even withstands pizza sauce and Coke™. So no more excuses about having to eat dinner instead of doing homework! Do both at the same time and have more time to watch television, play computer games or socialise with your friends! The Jumping Jiminy Journal is able to withstand the strain!

The handy organiser has a built-in memory chip. Once programmed, a flashing alarm and thoroughly annoying voice lets you know very loudly that you need to do some homework! Best of all there is a high-frequency portable attachment which may be carried with you. This will interrupt you no matter what you are doing and where you are to remind you about doing your homework! What a great bonus!

The Jumping Jiminy Journal comes with its own calculator and a supply of biros, pencils, erasers and blank paper. There is a convenient compartment for a mobile phone and a portable music player. It also has a handy shoulder pouch to allow you to carry it wherever you go!

This is by far the greatest invention since the school bell! Every pupil should have one and all parents will want to buy one for their child! The Jumping Jiminy Journal is easy to see, easy to hear, reliable, durable and convenient!

The Jumping Jiminy Journal! You need one! Get it now!

Examining discussion ③

Use the discussion on page 71 to complete the page.

1. Title

(a) Is the title of the discussion appropriate? **yes** ☐ **no** ☐

(b) Write an alternative title which would suit this discussion.

2. Introduction

(a) How many paragraphs make up the introduction? _____

(b) Why do you think the introduction is so long?

_____

_____

_____

(c) Tick the boxes.

(i) The introduction stated the issue. ☐

(ii) The introduction told what the writer wants to happen. ☐

3. Arguments

The writer gives a number of arguments to persuade readers to buy the journal.

(a) Write bullet points to show the main arguments presented.

- _____

  _____

- _____

  _____

- _____

  _____

(b) Were the arguments given in order from strongest to weakest?

yes ☐   **no** ☐

(c) Write the argument which you feel is the most important.

_____

_____

_____

(d) Write a sentence to give another argument for buying the journal.

4. Conclusion

(a) Did the writer restate his opinion?

yes ☐   **no** ☐

(b) Write the sentence which does this best.

_____

_____

_____

_____

1. Plan a discussion in the form of an advertisement for a portable music player.
   Be as creative as you wish!

Title

Introduction

Arguments

Don't forget to use persuasive language.

Conclusion

2. Write your discussion.

3. Edit your work.